J. RUSSELL SMITH

Geographer, Educator, and Conservationist

J. RUSSELL SMITH

oseph (handwritten)

Geographer, Educator,
and Conservationist

By

Virginia M. Rowley

Philadelphia: University of Pennsylvania Press

7449
Printed in the United States of America

Contents

Preface

AT THE END OF THE NINETEENTH CENTURY, REVOLUTIONARY developments began to take place in American geography. The humanization of the subject proceeded at a rapid pace, as did the application of geography to other fields. The changes were initiated at the college level, particularly in the schools of business, and later permeated the secondary and elementary levels.

Many American and European geographers participated in the growth of the content, method, and theory of modern geography. The specific purpose of this study is not biographical, but rather to explore the varied contributions of Professor J. Russell Smith to the development of human-economic geography and related fields in the United States.

The writer wishes to gratefully acknowledge the assistance of the following professors at Columbia University: the late George T. Renner, Jr., who suggested the topic, H. Phillip Bacon, her adviser; Erling Hunt, who offered many valuable suggestions, and the late Hubert Evans, who consistently showed interest in the study.

The writer is similarly grateful for the information and guidance given in interviews and letters by Professor J. Russell Smith and the late Mrs. Henrietta Stewart Smith, Professors Lester E. Klimn, Alfred H. Williams, and Joseph A. Willits, Charles A. Madison, Myra Light, and numerous other colleagues, students, and friends of Professor Smith. For assistance in proofreading, the writer wishes to express gratitude to Drs. Charles A. Rotunno and Morris H. Furman, Mary R. Furman, and Florence T. Rowley.

Facts are one thing, style and slant of writing are another. Dr. J. Russell Smith wrote no page or paragraph of the text of this book, unless that fact is shown by quotation marks. He never saw any of the author's manuscript or any of the publisher's galley proofs or page proofs.

V.M.R.

J. RUSSELL SMITH

Geographer, Educator, and Conservationist

I

Overview of Smith's Life and Work

JOSEPH RUSSELL SMITH WAS BORN IN LINCOLN, LOUDOUN County, Virginia, in 1874, of Quaker, middle-class, agricultural stock. This background and the experience of his formative years were influential in molding his personality and thinking.

QUAKER HERITAGE

Smith's Quaker ancestors emigrated to this country sometime between 1700 and 1740, during the "Golden Age of Quakerism in America."[1] Although the exact date is unknown, the family records told of a Smith family, including six children, that set sail from England.[2] The husband died en route; the rest of the family found a home in the colony of New Jersey.

The time was opportune for a successful settlement along the Atlantic seaboard. The most difficult phase of

[1]Howard Brinton, *Friends for 300 Years* (New York: Harper and Brothers, 1952), p. 183.
[2]Interview with Professor Smith, July 21, 1953.

11

the struggle to clear the wilderness and build homes was almost over. The French and Indian War—which was to bring a long period of disturbance to the colonies, and tension between Quakers and the home government in England—had not yet begun. The Quakers were influential in the government and cultural life of many parts of the colonies, including southern New Jersey.[3]

The flowering of Quakerism in the first half of the eighteenth century, which formed the moral base for future generations, was not characterized by any outburst of literary or artistic production. The most important product of Quakerism in the New World was the Quaker culture, which consisted of a clearly defined way of life with a rich, spiritual basis.[4]

Each Quaker community, well ordered and integrated, was a world unto itself. The center of life was the meeting, which handled matters of all kinds. Here, the poor were looked after, moral delinquents dealt with, and marriages performed. There was little need for a court, a police force, or officials of any kind except a few whose functions were to transfer property and to perform similar duties. Each meeting house also included a library and a school. The charter and moral code governing the community were written in the Book of Extracts,[5] which was subject to revision as new circumstances arose. The highly moral, democratic, and humanitarian qualities of Quaker-

[3]Rufus M. Jones, *The Quakers in the American Colonies* (London: Macmillan and Co., Limited, 1911), pp. 45–63, 111–302, 329–71; Thomas Jefferson Wertenbaker, *The Golden Age of Colonial Culture* (New York: New York University Press, 1942), pp. 62–82.

[4]Brinton, *Friends for 300 Years*, p. 184.

[5]This was the title given to the body of principles and rules governing the moral, political, and social life of a Quaker community.

ism were its inner strengths, and helped explain its influence and persistence as a movement.[6]

It was in this cultural atmosphere that the early American Quakers flourished, and in a similar one, generations later, that Smith grew to manhood. The Quaker tradition and training have stayed with him throughout his life. To this day he is an active Friend. The social awareness, the feeling for the community and the individuals who compose it, the concept of world brotherhood in a world freed from war, and other major themes in his writings reflected his Quaker heritage. Any work seemed comparatively unimportant to Smith if, in the end, it did not in some way involve man and serve as a means of improving his life on earth. As he stated: "I was born with two or three things. One of them was curiosity. I want to know. The other was a desire to help humanity. . . . Curiosity, helpfulness, and a desire to teach is the true essence of my spirit."[7] These desires found practical expression through his work in human-economic geography and applied fields.

Smith absorbed other Quaker characteristics. Simplicity always marked his speech, dress, and deportment. One of the qualities which made his books so popular and useful was his ability to write in easily understood terms. As Isaiah Bowman said of Smith's *North America*, "This is as interesting as a novel and really bridges the gap between technical jargon and the questioning mind that must have its knowledge in plain English."[8]

[6]Charles M. Woodman, *Quakers Find a Way, Their Discoveries in Practical Living* (Indianapolis: Bobbs--Merrill, 1950), p. 157.

[7]Interview with Professor Smith, July 21, 1953.

[8]Isaiah Bowman, Review of *North America* by J. Russell Smith, *Journal of Geography*, (July, 1925), 109.

Smith also consistently exhibited Quaker thrift and practicality. Through his writings and simple living he built up a substantial personal income. As for practicality, Smith always emphasized and lived his belief that facts and ideas in themselves were valueless; they gained worth only when they were put to practical use. Thus, the moral and cultural heritage of Quakerism must be taken into account in tracing the factors that influenced Smith.

CHILDHOOD IN NORTHERN VIRGINIA

In the late 1700's some of Smith's ancestors started moving south into the Appalachian Valley because New Jersey and Pennsylvania were becoming too crowded. They continued on into northern Virginia, stopping half way across Loudoun County when they encountered slave-owning southern farmers. Here they settled and began building prosperous farms on the fertile limestone soil. A new generation grew up, and in the early 1830's Thomas Smith, J. Russell Smith's father, was born. When Thomas Smith married, he and his wife, Ellen, moved to their newly purchased homestead near Lincoln, Virginia.[9] By 1861 they had a good farm and two daughters, Anna and Sara. The peaceful family life was soon disrupted, however, by the Civil War. Inevitably, the difference in belief and way of life between the small-farm, anti-slavery Quakers and Pennsylvania Germans, on the one hand, and the large-farm, slaveowning Southerners, on the other, caused the county to be split in loyalty between the North and the South. Two semi-guerrilla regiments were organized in the county—Moseby's the Southern, and Mean's, the Northern. Their raids periodically ravaged

[9]Interview with Professor Smith, July 14, 1953.

the countryside. Often, Thomas Smith had to go into hiding to escape retaliation for refusing to join one or the other guerrilla band. Then, too, because the Smith farm was in the strategic Shenandoah Valley, the roadway for both the Northern and Southern armies, they constantly felt the impact of invading troops.

Besides his early realization of the misery and suffering of conflict, gained from his parents' accounts of the Civil War, Smith received other insights from his farm boyhood, which helped shape his character and stimulate his interests. True to the Quaker tradition, he was taught the virtue of physical labor at a young age. As soon as he was old enough, he gathered eggs, fed the pigs and chickens, pulled weeds, and helped make the garden. Accordingly, Smith believed that, "A farm boy is living with the effects of his environment and so cause and effect is natural with him—more than with a city boy."[10] In later years, he appreciated this early training because it showed him the educational value of learning by doing and of seeking cause and effect relationships.

His closeness to the land also provided a readiness basis for his later interest in geography, conservation, and problems of agriculture. Smith stated:

Now always as far back as I can remember I have been interested in the earth as a place where people lived. The forest fire burns me, a gully hurts me—no matter whose land it is on. It is an injury to the human race. Now, I can't remember when these things didn't happen to me.[11]

Smith's interest in testing and experimentation was stimulated by working with his father. Besides being a

[10]*Ibid.*
[11]*Ibid.*

successful general farmer, Thomas Smith was also a bit
of a farm pioneer. Smith recalled:

My father was always doing small or simple experiments.
He didn't do any work in conservation. His work was largely
bringing new breeds of animals [and varieties of plants] into
the neighborhoood. . . . He wasn't a scientific experimenter.
. . . My father went to a country schoool about a hundred
years ago and his opportunity to get a scientific viewpoint was
fractional to what any boy now gets in any school. . . . The
chief thing he did was to find that somebody off somewhere
was using a new kind of wheat, and get some and plant it, or
a new kind of corn, and get some of it and plant it.[12]

In later years, Smith used a similar technique to find
new and better crop-bearing trees. In assessing his father's
influence, Smith concluded: "Perhaps from him I got a
certain tendency toward pioneering, if you can call my
work pioneering." [13]

Then, too, like a typical farm boy, Smith constantly
watched the weather. He also liked to measure rainfall
and study the growth of trees. More than once he got
into trouble with his mother for counting the number of
rings on logs that he should have been putting into the
fire. More important, though, following the lead of his
father, he was "not content to let a good idea lie." [14] The
practical application of the theoretical is another key to
his character and work.

EDUCATIONAL AND PROFESSIONAL BACKGROUND

Just as Smith's home environment helped to develop

[12]*Ibid.*
[13]*Ibid.*
[14]*Ibid.*

his character and innate abilities, his educational background channeled his interests and gave direction to his talents.

Educational Background

Smith received his elementary and secondary training in Quaker schools. Until he was seventeen he attended local schools in Lincoln. Then, for a year, he went to the Abington Friends School in Jenkintown, Pennsylvania, to finish his preparation for college.

Even though most of Smith's early education was sectarian and of the "little red schoolhouse" variety, it was far from being inferior and narrow. Since education was not only one of the chief ways of assuring the survival of the faith, but also of advancing in the world, it was a fundamental part of Quaker culture.[15] The Quakers built their educational system on the modern premise that schools should be democratic and concerned with the needs of children. They were among the pioneers in the equal education of boys and girls, the use of nonviolent methods of discipline, and the introduction of science and practical subjects into the curriculum.[16] The Quakers also strove to develop a sense of belonging to a religious community and a desire for simplicity and moderation in dress, speech, and deportment.

Furthermore, Smith attended Quaker schools of the more liberal Hicksite sect that emphasized reliance on the individual rather than on a hierarchy, and the supremacy of mystical experience over the rigid dictation of Scripture. Subsequently, the Hicksites more readily permitted

[15]Howard Brinton, *Quaker Education in Theory and Practice* (Pendle Hill, Pa.: 1940), pp. 50–52.

[16]Brinton, *Quaker Education in Theory and Practice*, pp. 52–53.

their traditional mysticism to be replaced by the newer rationalism of the late nineteenth and twentieth centuries.[17]

During his childhood, however, Smith seldom thought about doctrinal differences. He made use of the books in his home and in the small library of the Friends' Meeting House, but he did not concentrate too heavily on them. He went to school, did his lessons, played like other boys, and read quite a bit on miscellaneous subjects. His parents had no specific profession selected for him. They provided him with the best schools they could and a fairly large library at home, but they were more interested in having him grow up in a normal way.[18]

From his early school years, Smith remembered certain teachers, such as Edward B. Rawson, to whom he attributed a good deal of influence during adolescence. Smith said of this engineer turned teacher that "he was not so much a hail-fellow-well-met as one whose principles I admired. He fed my interest but he didn't make it." [19] It appeared that Rawson used an experimental approach in a good deal of his science teaching. Smith told of his interesting demonstrations of physical principles with simple, homemade devices, and his use of field trips.

Although Smith loved nature, the subject of geography was not a vital part of his life until much later. However, he had a liking for the subject even at an early age. His mother, who had the reputation of being "quite scholarly and one of the best-read people in the county," [20] used to play map games with him long before he entered school. Smith related:

[17]Brinton, *Friends for 300 Years*, p. 151.
[18]Interview with Professor Smith, July 14, 1953.
[19]*Ibid.*
[20]*Ibid.*

I remember once I went and climbed into her bed and rehearsed the very startling fact that San Salvador was the capital of Salvador, and Guatemala was the capital of Guatemala, and that Tegucigalpa was the capital of Honduras. I thought it strange that countries should have cities with names like that. Tegucigalpa made you think of a goose galloping which sounded very awkward. That's my first memory of geography.[21]

Smith's mother did not deliberately foster an interest in geography. She merely participated in what happened to interest her son at the time. In fact, geography was held in such low esteem that Smith said, perhaps jokingly, when he became a specialist in the field he sometimes believed his mother was

. . . a bit ashamed of me—the idea of a man teaching geography! Why that was something for kids. I am sure that if I had told her that I was a professor of Latin she would have thought I was a more scholarly person. Geography—she had had geography when she went to grammar school—a little book.[22]

Smith had formal geography in school, especially in the sixth grade where he was introduced to Swinton's texts. However, it was the typical political geography of the time, consisting of place names and boundaries to be memorized by rote. Above the elementary level, geography had no real status.

When considering a major in college, Smith's choice was economics because, as he explained:

You must not forget George Washington and Thomas

[21]*Ibid.*
[22]*Ibid.*

Jefferson were farmers and they helped to govern the United
States. Wasn't it the proper ambition for a young farm boy
to want to help govern the United States? If I were going
to be in politics, I would have to know economics—so that I
would know better how to govern the United States. I
wanted economics to be an effective citizen.[23]

This may have been odd reasoning, but it demonstrated
the ambitious and practical turn of his nature. He believed
that economics was of utility in attaining the wealth that
begets influence, so he chose this field together with
supplementary courses in public and business law, history,
and political science.

From Economics to Geography

In keeping with his decision, Smith entered the Wharton School of Finance and Economy of the University
of Pennsylvania in 1893. In the rich academic atmosphere
of this school Smith found fresh stimulation from such
teachers as Edmund J. James, Professor of Political
Science and later President of the University of Illinois,
and Simon N. Patten, Professor of Economics. Patten influenced him to seek for "the significance of things." So,
too, did James, whom Smith described as follows:

[James would] quote such and such clause of the Constitution, and then he would make you tell what it meant. We
would spend an hour or more on what that one clause of the
Constitution meant. Perhaps that was good training to get the
habit of appreciating the significance of facts. That is what
geography is for if it is well done, because it must be a cause
and effect relationship—a matter of significance. James was

[23]*Ibid.*

talking about the Constitution of the United States but it was a method he helped give me—an attitude.[24]

It is interesting that Smith attended only his freshman year of 1893-94 in full. For his work he received the mark of "D," which was equivalent to distinguished. In order to earn money for his education he taught full-time in various high schools from 1894 to 1899. He did not return to full-time study at the Wharton School until his senior year in 1897. During that year he passed all the required courses, on the average of one a month, by taking written examinations, a procedure in vogue at the time. In 1898 he received his B.A. as well as the Terry Prize for distinguished scholarship.[25] He then began studying for a Master's degree in economics under Emory R. Johnson.

Until this time Smith had no inkling of his future career in geography. He said:

I had no idea when I graduated from college that I would be anything other than an economist, which was the natural direction of one graduating from the Wharton School with an academic type of mind. . . .

The thing that really made me a geographer was an accidental governmental position. I was going along teaching history and taking graduate study, looking forward to being an economist, when the question arose in the United States Senate: Where shall we build a canal across the American isthmus?[26]

The chance job that changed Smith's life was the one

[24]*Ibid.*

[25]Taken from the scholastic records of Smith included in the Archives of the University of Pennsylvania.

[26]Interview with Professor Smith, July 14, 1953.

with the Isthmian Canal Commission. In 1899 Congress appropriated a million dollars for a commission to investigate routes for a canal across the Isthmus of Panama and to determine which was the most practical and feasible.[27]

The working commission consisted of seven engineers in charge of construction and an economist to estimate the possible cost of an Isthmian canal. The economist was Emory R. Johnson of the Wharton School. Johnson, in turn, hired Smith, one of his students, as his assistant. Since able, industrious, and imaginative men were needed for the job, Johnson's choice was an open recognition of Smith's ability. Johnson was the most important influence on Smith during his student days at Wharton, not only because he chose Smith for the commission, but also because he gave him his start in college teaching.

Not only did Johnson and Smith have to judge costs and evaluate routes and methods of construction, they also had to estimate what the traffic would be when the canal was completed. This called for a definite approximation of present and future resources and industries. In other words, it required a wide knowledge of the geography of world trade and of the specific countries that would use the canal.

Johnson and Smith had little formal training in geography beyond what they had studied in elementary school. Smith recalled:

We floundered like a pair of landlubbers in the mud trying to swim. We wasted time horribly, but we finally came up with a good estimate; . . . our chore in trying to find facts in the literature of 1899 was a tough one. . . . We came out of that job with a firm conviction that the American educational

[27]*Report of the Isthmian Canal Commission, 1899–1901* (Washington: Government Printing Office, 1904), p. 11.

field needed geography in the colleges—quick. Because of our helplessness in the face of a concrete problem, it convinced us that it was extremely important. . . .

I decided I was going to be a geographer. I didn't know if I could get a job in a college, but I knew I could get a job in a high school.[28]

Graduate Study at Leipzig

Smith carried through with his resolve. He left the commission, drew his last check on July 31, 1901, and that same afternoon sailed from New York with his wife Henrietta.[29] His destination was the University of Leipzig where Friedrich Ratzel was doing outstanding work in geography.

For one interested in learning geography at the turn of the century, Ratzel was the logical teacher because of his pre-eminence in the field. It is possible that Smith's early, somewhat deterministic approach may be traced to this German geographer. Smith, however, never attributed any direct influence either to Ratzel or to Ratzel's colleague, Karl Sapper, his other professor at Leipzig. Sapper was not only a geographer of the first rank, but also an ethnologist famous for his original work in Central America and Mexico.

Although Smith considered Ratzel and Sapper fine men and remarkable scholars, Smith did not come back worshipping Germany.[30] His disappointment stemmed largely from his poor command of the German language, his lack of interest and training in German culture, and his distaste for Prussian militarism.

[28]Interview with Professor Smith, July 14, 1953.
[29]Mrs. Henrietta Smith died in 1962.
[30]Interview with Professor Smith, July 14, 1953.

Another reason for Smith's dissatisfaction was his meager background in geography other than the research work done for the Isthmian Canal Commission. He was completely unprepared for Ratzel's scholarly and technical presentation of anthropogeography, and probably got more from Semple's translations than from Ratzel himself. Later, Smith regretted that he had not studied at Oxford under Herbertson, whose world scheme of natural regions was subsequently influential in his own writings.[31]

Of much more significance to Smith were the twelve weeks of summer vacation spent studying the trade, port, and shipping conditions in leading European cities.[32] This practical field work together with his study of ocean freight rates and the commercial effects of the canal, made while working with the commission, pointed the way to his initial development. It was evident that his primary interest was in practical aspects of geography, especially in reference to economics and commerce, rather than in the theoretical investigation of geographic phenomena. His further graduate study and early writings also emphasized this orientation. Upon returning from Europe, he accepted a fellowship in economics at the Wharton School for 1902–03, and in 1903 received his doctorate in economic geography. His dissertation, "The Organization of Ocean Commerce," was an applied economic–geographic study rather than a piece of pure, theoretical research.

Career in Teaching

Smith's career as a teacher began in the Abington Friends School in Jenkintown, Pennsylvania, where he

[31]*Ibid.*
[32]Such cities as London, Liverpool, Glasgow, Antwerp, Rotterdam, Hamburg, Bremen, and Genoa.

taught history during 1894–95. From there he moved to the George School in Newtown, Pennsylvania, where he taught history from 1896 to 1899. During this time, he taught only to finance his education. His interest in teaching as a career was aroused only after his work on the commission.

In 1903 he accepted the position of Instructor in Commerce at the Wharton School of the University of Pennsylvania, and from that time his life's work was set. He rapidly rose to be full professor in charge of the Department of Geography and Industry which was his own creation. At Wharton his writings and teaching helped give organization, meaning, and content to the new fields of human-economic geography and industrial management.

In 1919 he accepted the position of Professor of Economic Geography in charge of the department, at Columbia's School of Business. Here he continued his creative work in developing courses in regional economic geography. He also expanded his field of writing by producing *North America* and two of his three series of elementary geography texts. Although he retired from active teaching in 1944, he continued to write and completed his third series of texts several years later.

Work In Applied Fields

Smith was always interested in the practical application of geography to other fields. He was among those who early demonstrated that a knowledge of geographic factors could give greater meaning and efficiency to business operations and industrial management.

His major interest, however, was in the related areas of conservation and plant genetics. In these fields, he did important work by helping to develop awareness of the need for conserving natural resources and by breeding crop-bearing trees that could be used to prevent erosion and provide food for human beings and animals. Smith was also particularly active in such conservation groups as the Northern Nut Growers Association and Friends of the Land, the latter of which he helped found.

Professional Organizations

Smith was a member of various professional organizations. Chief among the professional geography groups with which he worked were: Association of American Geographers, National Council for Geographic Education, American Geographical Society, Pennsylvania Council of Geography Teachers, Southeastern Pennsylvania Geography Club, and International Geographical Union. The major education societies to which he belonged were: National Education Association, National Council for the Study of Education, and World Federation of Education Associations. During the years, Smith actively participated in many of these groups, giving speeches, writing articles for their journals, and serving on committees.

An Overview of Contributions

Smith's work, therefore may be divided into four broad, interrelated areas—advanced geographic writings, undergraduate and graduate teaching, elementary textbook writing, and work in applied fields. In each area he made important contributions, because of his dynamic, wide-ranging interests, his ability to synthesize and correlate material, his stimulating literary style, and his realization of the long-range, ethical objectives of all learning.

II

The Development of Human
Geography in the United States

TO SEE SMITH'S WORK IN THE CORRECT PERSPECTIVE, IT IS
necessary to evaluate it against the framework of the over-
all development of human geography in the United States.
Differences in geographic orientation resulting from a
diversity of training, experience, and interest were evident
in the development of American as well as European
geographers. Some were schooled in physiography and geology and, therefore, emphasized the physical aspects of
the science. Others, like Smith, were trained in the social
sciences and thus developed a greater interest in the
human aspects of geography.

William Morris Davis

William Morris Davis is usually considered the founding father of American geography. In paying tribute to
Davis after his death, the National Council for Geographic
Education voiced a typical estimate that "he exerted
greater influence on scientific geography and on educa-

tional geography from the elementary school to the university than has any other American scholar." [1] Davis' work and that of Shaler, his teacher and colleague, not only established geography on the college level, but also helped reorient it in the elementary and secondary schools from emphasis on political and statistical facts to concern for physiography and scientific explanation.

At the end of the 1890's, Davis' concept of geography changed to keep pace with the needs of the time. Instead of emphasizing the purely physical description of the earth, rooted in geomorphology, he began to state in his writings that geography was "the study of the environment in relation to man. . . . Pupils should be led . . . to perceive the character of the various geographic influences by which settlement, occupation, etc., have been determined." [2] Davis was evolving the concept of environmentalism, of physical controls and organic responses, and thus the next stage in the development of geography, that of biogeography or ontography, was initiated.[3]

Davis' advocacy of the relationship concept caught fire and was grasped by human, physical, and political geographers alike. Its almost literal and unquestioned acceptance was prompted by the newness of the science and the resulting confusion of many geographers as to its meaning. Davis' theory gave them a much desired formula or basis for procedure. His influence was apparent in the writings of Rollin D. Salisbury, Ralph S. Tarr, Albert Perry Brigham, Harlan H. Barrows, Walter S. Tower,

[1] Richard Elwood Dodge, "William Morris Davis—An Appreciation," *Journal of Geography*, XXXIII (April, 1934), 148.

[2] William Morris Davis, "The Present Trend of Geography," *111th Annual Report of the University of the State of New York* (1898), p. 196.

[3] William Morris Davis, "Systematic Geography," *Proceedings of the American Philosophical Society*, XL (April 3, 1902), 253–58.

George C. Chisholm, Richard Elwood Dodge, Smith, and many other geographers, during the first decade of the century.

ENVIRONMENTAL DETERMINATION

Unfortunately, as often happens with a new definition, enthusiasm ran riot and extreme positions dominated for a time. True, Davis tried to humanize physiography by formulating a concept of the interrelationship between life and earth, but in so doing, he made the earth the all-important factor, while life was reduced to a mechanical response to the physical environment. The most popular terms were geographic influence and human response, with environmental determinism ruling the day.[4]

The deterministic and mechanistic view of geography was both a reflection of the thinking of German geographers and an outgrowth of "social Darwinism." The latter, especially, had heavily colored the intellectual atmosphere of the United States for more than a quarter of a century.[5] A geography of environmental controls rested on the false assumption of a mechanical and unbroken chain of causation linking the physical phenomena of the earth's surface, the organic realm, and human society. Davis' later works, and those of his followers, showed frequent evidence of this distortion of evolutionary thought. It was almost impossible for any geographer of this early period to escape some imprint of the pre-

[4]Isaiah Bowman, "Commercial Geography as a Science, Reflections on Some Recent Books," *Geographical Review*, XV (April, 1925), 286.
[5]John Leighly, "What Has Happened to Physical Geography?" *Annals of the Association of American Geographers*, XLV (December, 1955), 311–13. See also Richard Hofstadter, *Social Darwinism in American Thought* (Boston: The Beacon Press, 1958), pp. 13–57, 85–170.

dominantly deterministic tone of the time. Some of Smith's early writings, for example, revealed manifestations of determinism which his later works, emphasizing as they did man's will in shaping his world, would seem to belie.[6]

The Weakening of Environmental Determinism

The gradual weakening of the hold of physical determinism came through the development of human geography and allied fields. At the turn of the century, when Davis' influence rose to its peak, mechanical, monistic interpretation was gradually becoming outdated because of advances in psychology, anthropology, economics, and social philosophy.[7] "It was rendered obsolete by the recognition that in human societies processes of an order different from the mechanical order are at work, processes that cannot be comprehended even by the categories applicable to organic phenomena."[8] This did not mean that the relationship concept in geography was abandoned. Rather, the emphasis was broadened from mechanical life responses to a mutual interrelationship between earth and man. This change implied not only the adaptation of man to his environment, but also man's increasing adaptation of the environment to his needs through technological advances. It also meant a more accurate interpretation of Darwin's theory of evolution in place of its distortion into mechanical causation.

Indications of the trend toward a broadened human geography were evident in the membership and proceed-

[6]Smith, "Economic Geography and Its Relation to Economic Theory and Higher Education," pp. 473–75.

[7]Hofstadter, Social Darwinism in American Thought, pp. 67–85, 105–23.

[8]Leighly, "What Has Happened to Physical Geography?" p. 313.

ings of the Association of American Geographers. In 1904 most of the members were geologists and physical geographers. Toward the end of the first decade of the century, the balance shifted in favor of the human geographers. As Ray H. Whitbeck commented in tracing the development of geography through the changing climate of opinion in the Association of American Geographers:

In the future development of the science, human geography will be the dominating aspect, mainly because people are more interested in the doings of mankind than they are in the distribution of plants, animals, and minerals, or in the evolution of the surface features of the earth.[9]

The articles in the *Journal of Geography* and other geographical publications gave further evidence of the change, as did the work done at the university level, during the first two decades of the century. (See Appendix, pp. 221–31.)

Influence of European Human Geographers

A good deal of the momentum toward human geography had its origin in the words of European geographers. This was especially true of the work of the French "possibilists" headed by Paul Vidal de la Blache and Jean Brunhes and that of the English group, the latter led by Andrew J. Herbertson, J. Scott Keltie, Halford J. Mackinder, John F. Unstead, and Eva G. Taylor. Some American geographers, Smith among them, gave much credit to the English leaders, particularly Herbertson. His books,

[9] Ray H. Whitbeck, "Adjustments to Environment in South America: An Interplay of Influences," *Annals of the Association of American Gographers*, XVI (March, 1926), 3.

such as *Man and His Work*,[10] had a wide circulation in the United States and were the forerunners of books on the "new geography," because they were both human and regional in orientation.

Many American geographers who worked in the early decades of the century helped develop human geography by weakening the hold of physical determinism and broadening the content base and methodology of the field. The writings of Walter Sheldon Tower, a colleague of Smith at Pennsylvania and an active geographic theorist of the time, illustrated the diminishing influence of physical determinism. In 1904, Tower emphasized that geography must include:

. . . the explanation of every condition of life in so far as it has been determined or modified by the physical environment. It must give the responses of man in his activities, social, political, historical and economic; of plants and of animals, in their distribution, selection, and adaptation.[11]

Two years later, however, Tower made a strong plea against the submergence of the human element by physiographic conditions and advocated broadening the environmental base to include climate and basic human factors, in addition to landforms.[12] Confirmation was added to

[10]Andrew J. Herbertson, *Man and His Work; An Introduction to Human Geography* (London: A. and C. Black, 1893).

[11]Walter Sheldon Tower, "A Field for Studies in Regional Geography," *Bulletin of the American Geographical Society*, XXXVIII (August, 1906), 488.

[12]Walter Sheldon Tower, "The Human Side of Systematic Geography," *Bulletin of the American Geographical Society*, XL (September, 1908), 525–26.

Tower's ideas by Ray H. Whitbeck, who, among others, also believed that too much emphasis was placed on the detailed study and classification of landforms.[13]

Wolfgang L. G. Joerg maintained that geography must be studied through a regional focus and considered the natural region to be a composite of structural, climatic, vegetational, and zoological elements.[14] Important, too, in spreading the new ideas were the works of Ellsworth T. Huntington, which analyzed the relationship between climatic factors and cultural patterns.

Isaiah Bowman and Albert Perry Brigham, other pioneers, similarly sounded the trend of the new development. For example, Brigham read a paper at the opening of a round-table conference of the Association of American Geographers in 1909, that stressed the all-encompassing nature of geography. He believed that geography served as a bridge between the natural and social sciences and was basic to the scientific study of human society. Accordingly, he maintained that geography should draw its data from all the sciences dealing with man and nature. Like Tower, Brigham held the unreserved belief that

. . . the physical and the organic are co-ordinate parts of geography and both distribution and relation belong to its concept, freely conceding that the highest synthesis of material and the chief goal of study lie in the field of relation of earth to life and preeminently in the bond between man and his total environment.[15]

[13]Ray H. Whitbeck, "The Present Trend of Geography in the United States," *Geographical Journal*, XXXV (April, 1910), 420–25.

[14]Wolfgang L. G. Joerg, "The Subdivision of North America into Natural Regions: A Preliminary Inquiry," *Annals of the Association of American Geographers*, IV (1914), 56–58.

[15]Albert Perry Brigham, "The Organic Side of Geography: Its Nature and Its Limits," *Bulletin of the American Geographical Society*, XLII (June, 1910), 442.

In paying tribute to Brigham on his seventy-fifth birth-
day, members of the Association of American Geographers
recognized that he had consistently sounded a warning
against geographic determinism.[16]

Another important indication of the trend during this
period was George B. Roorbach's 1914 study which dealt
with the results of an inquiry made of leading geographers
as to the meaning of geography and the most urgent
problems which needed investigation.[17] A major conclusion reached was that

. . . geography concerns itself with the study of the relationship between earth and life, particularly human life. There
is a considerable difference of opinion as to just what lines of
investigation should be followed, but almost general agreement that the aim of geographical work . . . is to establish
the fact of, and deduce the principles underlying, this relationship between the physical earth and its inhabiting organisms.[18]

Roorbach cited Brigham's statement that "the real goal
and heart of our science is in the field of human geography,"[19] as typical of most of the responses.

Among the important considerations that still had to be

[16]Ray H. Whitbeck, "Human Geographer," *Annals of the Association
of American Geographers,* XX (June, 1950), 77–80. The entire June,
1930 issue of the *Annals* is devoted to articles by leading geographers
on different aspects of Brigham's career.

[17]George B. Roorbach, "The Trend of Modern Geography, A Symposium," *Bulletin of the American Geographical Society,* XLVI (November, 1914), 798–808. Among the geographers questioned were:
Wallace W. Atwood, Isaiah Bowman, Albert Perry Brigham, Richard Elwood Dodge, Nevin M. Fenneman, Henry Gannett, George D. Hubbard,
Ellsworth Huntington, Mark Jefferson, Wolfgang L. G. Joerg, J. Scott
Keltie, Rollin D. Salisbury, J. Russell Smith, and Ray H. Whitbeck.

[18]Roorbach, "The Trend of Modern Geography, A Symposium," p.
802.

[19]*Ibid.*

developed were: regional geographic studies, especially a regional geography of North America, and the further definition and organization of geographic materials. Through his writings in economic and regional geography, Smith helped meet these needs. It was interesting to note that of the twenty-nine geographers questioned, only Wallace W. Atwood and Nevin M. Fenneman listed problems in physical geography as most important.

HUMAN ECOLOGY

Although human geography received great impetus in the first two decades of the new century, environmentalism was not really abandoned until the late 1920's. The first of the new definitions to attract widespread attention after World War I was still tinged with it. This was the definition that Barrows gave in his presidential address before the Association of American Geographers in 1922, entitled "Geography as Human Ecology." [20] Since geography had long been defined in rather ecologic terms,[21] Barrows was probably not completely wrong in ascribing to American geographers a definition of their subject, "as dealing solely with the mutual relations between man and his natural environment." [22] He, like others, saw the fallacy of extreme physical causation; however, he ascribed too much determinism to the human factor. Thus, Barrows' concept of geography was a backward step since he narrowed the scope of geography as drawn by Brigham, Fenneman,[23] and others who now conceived of geog-

[20]Harlan H. Barrows, "Geography as Human Ecology," *Annals of the Association of American Geographers*, XIII (March, 1923), 1–13.
[21]J. Paul Goode, "A College Course in Ontography," *Annals of the Association of American Geographers*, I (1911), 111.
[22]Barrows, "Geography as Human Ecology," p. 3.
[23]Nevin M. Fenneman, "The Circumference of Geography," *Annals of the Association of American Geographers*, IX (1919), 3–11.

raphy as a synthetic areal sciene. In effect, Barrows eliminated all aspects of physical geography or any other study not dealing explicitly with man. Moreover, he exhibited an economic determinism, operating in the mechanistic spirit of social Darwinism, just as Davis had with physiography, since he believed that "upon economic geography for the most part the other divisions of the subject must be based." [24]

Weakening of Barrows' Human Ecology

Barrows' ideas were influential at first, but gradually their acceptance was challenged by the emergence of new elements. In commenting on Barrows' definition, Ray H. Whitbeck said in his presidential address before the Association of American Geographers in 1926 that:

If geography be restricted solely to the mutual relations between man and the natural environment, then any descriptive account of the earth's surface is not geography. . . . It is self-evident that before one can study the mutual relations between man and his natural environment, he must somewhere have learned of what the environment is made up. . . . All the weight of past practice, of the historical development of the science, of common usage and common understanding has included physical geography as part of geography.[25]

While Whitbeck agreed with Barrows' recognition of the human factor and the reality of human control instead of submission, he and many others could not accept the extreme position that defined geography as exclusively the

[24]Barrows, "Geography as Human Ecology," p. 13.
[25]Whitbeck, "Adjustments to Environment in South America: An Interplay of Infuences," 5–6.

interrelationship between man and his natural environment as seen through a chiefly economic focus .

In tempering the influence of Barrows' exteme presentation, credit must again be given to the French possibilistic school of geographers lead by Vidal de la Blache and Brunhes, whose work broadened the perspective of American human and regional geographers. Both men saw the necessity for detailed synthetic studies in geography which, in turn, gave rise to a number of regional monographs. After the first decade of the twentieth century, their books gained strong recognition in America. As accurate regional maps developed and detailed research proceeded, the disciples of the French School became increasingly numerous in the United States.

THE SURVEY METHOD AND REGIONAL GEOGRAPHY

Toward the end of the mid-1920's, in the spirit of the French possibilists, rapid developments took place in the use of statistics and field mapping in studying regional geographic patterns. The leader of the new methodology was Carl O. Sauer of the University of California. Sauer and his followers rejected the hypothesis of mechanical causation in human affairs that had so long restricted American geographic thought. His work provided a guide for innumerable regional studies of small areas.[26] Sauer's method was anthropocentric, but at the same time he recognized that physical geography was important to his program and he used it to select those items which represented the background and medium of human activities.

[26]Carl O. Sauer, "The Survey Method in Geography and Its Objectives," *Annals of the Association of American Geographers,* XIV (March, 1924), 17–19.

In his "Morphology of Landscape," [27] Sauer rejected the rational interpretation of physical formation, but he could not relinquish, as Barrows had, the actual field investigation of the physical and cultural landscapes, for a purely theoretical and untested relation between the two.

Regional Geography Comes Into Its Own

In the 1920's the description and analysis of regions became the main focus of geographical writings in the United States. A report of the Conference on Regions of the Association of American Geographers in 1935 was indicative of the thinking of the time that:

The major contribution of geography to the general field of science is the recognition, first, of the ever-varying aspect of the land, and secondly, that, in spite of this variation, the land tends to be divided into areas of more or less similarity. Such areas we call regions. . . .

In geography, the region forms the basis of what is now termed modern or regional geography and has come to be widely accepted as the culminating branch of the subject.[28]

MODERN GEOGRAPHY—THE STUDY OF
AREAL DIFFERENTIATION

Since the turn of the century American geography has been plagued by a duality between human and physical

[27]Carl O. Sauer, *The Morphology of Landscape* (University of California Publications in Geography, Vol. II, No. 2. Berkeley, California: University of California Press, 1925), pp. 19–53.
[28]Robert Burnett Hall, "The Geographic Region: A Résumé," *Annals of the Association of American Geographers*, XXV (September, 1935), 122–23.

aspects of the subject. Today, there has developed a growing recognition that there is but one landscape with geography increasingly defined as the study of areal differentiation.[29] This concept encompasses all phases of the region, natural and human, which aid in its analysis. Thus, both human and physical elements are united in the quest to discern the characteristics of areal composites— the central phenomenon of geographic science.

More and more, too, geography had become practical or applied, with ever-ramifying branches to meet the changing needs of the time. In this way, geography is realizing one of its highest functions: that of aiding man to understand his world and to make wiser use of its resources.

[29]Preston E. James and Clarence F. Jones, (eds.), *American Geography: Inventory and Prospect* (Syracuse University Press, 1954), pp. 7–8.

III

Smith's Contributions to Human, Economic, and Regional Geography

THIS CHAPTER EXPLORES SMITH'S ROLE IN THE DEVELOPMENT of human, economic, and regional geography in America, through an analysis of his advanced writings. Not only did Smith grow in compass of interest, from limited beginnings in strictly commercial and trade affairs to many aspects of geography and allied fields, but also, he continually showed a developing maturity in basic geographic attitudes and concepts.

SMITH'S CHANGING VIEWS

When Smith published his first article in 1899, his thinking was in certain respects quite different from that of two decades or so later. In 1899, he strongly favored our abandoning the newly acquired Philippine Islands. Instead, he proposed that we develop our own country and our trade relations with Latin America, which was nearer at hand and more varied in natural resources. His rejection of the Philippine Islands reflected the then current feeling of the "inferiority" of the Filipino people as shown by his statement: "While we deem the Chinese so undesirable that we exclude him from our shores, all authorities agree that his race is superior to that of the Malays, Tagols, and Negritos who inhabit the Philippines." [1] He closed with an isolationist blast:

The American policy of our forefathers is one for us. . . . America is an industrial unit, an economic unit, full of undeveloped possibilities that await the hand of American enterprise. The continent is controlled by the most ingenious of all races, and is dominated by the highest political ideals known to man. What need have we to reach out across seven thousand miles of ocean to take lands populous with millions of barbarians?[2]

Smith still reflected the racism and narrow prejudice of the time in an article written in 1907 where he stated:

A knowledge of resource and of industry must be reinforced by some knowledge of the industrial qualities and equipment of peoples. They vary greatly. . . . I shall not discuss here the probable origin of the work quality in races, but it is probable that this trait of the white . . . man comes as slowly as civilization itself. . . . Yet, entirely overlooking this quality, millions of Americans enthusiastically voted for . . . extending to another race, the Filipinos, the blessings of American liberty and civilization.[3]

It seemed almost as if another man were speaking in

[1] J. Russell Smith, "The Philippine Islands and American Capital," *Popular Science Monthly*, LX (June, 1899), 188.
[2] Smith, "The Philippine Islands and American Capital," 192.
[3] J. Russell Smith, "Economic Geography and Its Relation to Economic Theory and Higher Education," *Bulletin of the American Geographical Society*, XXXIX (August, 1907), 477–78.

Geography and the Higher Citzenship,[4] a 1925 pamphlet containing three articles that dealt with the teaching of geography in elementary schools. Here, Smith advocated respect, sympathy, and understanding of all peoples as major objectives of geographic education. The following statement was typical of a reorientation that had previously begun in his thinking near the end of the first decade of the century:

Not only is an understanding of geography a vital part of training for citizenship in any country but it is the chief opportunity in our schools for teaching the higher citizenship—the relations, the good relations of the nations with each other as nations.[5]

Smith's sharp change in attitude probably resulted from a broadening of interest from the initial fields of trade and commerce to the varied and dynamic study of relationships between man and his environment, as the basis of cultural patterns. Other factors were his own developing maturity and the changing temper of the times. The devastations of World War I, in particular, caused Smith to lose his world, "the fool's paradise," [6] as he called it, of the pre-1914 days. The war demonstrated to him, as it had to many others, the horrible result of lack of world understanding and common brotherhood. The theme of world citizenship which some of our diplomats and educators are only grasping today, though not original with Smith, has been one of his major goals since the early years of the country.[7]

[4]J. Russell Smith, *Geography and the Higher Citizenship* (Philadelphia: The John C. Winston Co., 1925).
[5]*Ibid.*, p. 3.
[6]*Ibid.*, p. 1.
[7]J. Russell Smith, "Geography and World Citizenship," *Social Education,* XXI (May, 1957), 205.

In general, Smith's works did not show great originality or theoretical insight. At times, though, he exhibited a creativity and an ability to synthesize ideas which marked him as one of the pioneers of American geography.

ECONOMIC GEOGRAPHY BEFORE SMITH

Most of Smith's contributions to human geography were through its economic aspects. Although economic geography was relatively unorganized before Smith's time and chiefly commercial in outlook, it had long attracted a small but persistent interest in the United States. Economics and allied subjects were practical and suited the mood of the young nation, the development of which was based on the application of technology to the utilization of vast natural resources. As early as 1859, the articles in the first ten issues of the *Journal of the American Geographical Society*[8] exhibited a lively interest in economic activities and natural resources. So did the early geographic and geological surveys of Henry Gannett, F. V. Hayden, Major John W. Powell, Captain George M. Wheeler, and others, who had much in common with economic geographers of the early 1900's.

The first article on commercial geography was published in 1888.[9] Near the turn of the century, writings in commercial geography became more abundant. In 1891, John N. Tilden,[10] and in 1902, Cyrus C. Adams[11] wrote

[8]From 1859 to 1900, the *Bulletin of the American Geographical Society*, when bound, was called the *Journal of the American Geographical Society*.

[9]Charles H. Stockton, "The Commercial Geography of the American Interoceanic Canal," *Journal of the American Geographical Society*, XX (June, 1888), 75–93.

[10]John N. Tilden, *Commercial Geography for Academies, High Schools, and Business Colleges* (Boston: Leach, Shewell, and Sanborn, 1891).

[11]Cyrus C. Adams, *An Elementary Commercial Geography* (New York: D. Appleton & Co., 1902).

texts on commercial geography. Adams showed further
interest in the field by publishing a number of articles in
the *Journal of the American Geographical Society,* of
which he was the editor.

The year 1900 was more important, however, because
for the first time, the term "economic geography" was
used in American writings.[12] The new usage exhibited the
growth of the field which began to include a study of man
in relation to all economic activities instead of just commercial relations. The following year, L. H. Keasbey wrote
two articles[13] on the content and function of economic
geography. Thus, in the first decade of the twentieth
century when Smith began to write, commercial geography, focused on trade in commodities, was gradually
encompassed within the larger sphere of economic geography.

SMITH'S EARLY WRITINGS

Smith's initial writings were rather narrow and descriptive, typical of commercial geography at the time; however, his diversity of themes indicated a growing breadth
and maturity of insight. These early works can be divided
into three main categories on the basis of subject matter
treated.

One group, an outgrowth of his trip abroad in 1901–02,
included a series of articles on commercial administration
and port facilities of various European countries.[14] There

[12]Ellen Churchill Semple, "Louisville: A Study in Economic Geography," *Journal of School Geography,* IV (December, 1900), 361–70.
[13]L. M. Keasbey, "The Study of Economic Geography" and "The
Principles of Economic Geography," *Political Science Quarterly,* XVI
(March, 1901), 79–95, 476–85.
[14]These articles include: "The British System of Commercial Administration," *Annals of the American Academy of Political and Social
Science,* XXIV (November, 1904), 507–25; "Harbor Facilities of Lon-

was nothing new or outstanding about these papers, the titles being self-explanatory, but the articles showed manifestations of Smith's growing awareness of the role of geographic and historical factors in causing different commercial growth patterns.

The second group of publications[15] grew out of his activities with the Isthmian Canal Commission from 1899 to 1901. The basic work was *The Organization of Ocean Commerce*, 1905, which inspired many of the other writings in the group. To a large extent, the substance of the second group of articles was incorporated into Part II of *Industrial and Commercial Geography*[16] under the headings, "Laws of Trade" and "The World Highway, The Ocean and Its Carriers." Smith also used these commercial studies as reading assignments for his courses at the University of Pennsylvania.

For the most part, *The Organization of Ocean Commerce* and *The Ocean Carrier*, the two books in this series on ocean commerce, contributed little to the development of the theoretical aspects of commercial or economic geography. They were confined largely to the presentation of facts and the description of processes in the business of ocean transportation and commerce. Unlike Smith's later works, they were dry in style. Their value stemmed from

don," *Annals of the American Academy of Political and Social Science*, XXIX (March, 1907), 386–89; "The Development of Commercial Centers," *Bulletin of the American Geographical Society*, XLII (May, 1910), 346–55; "The World Entrepot," *Journal of Political Economy*, XVII (November, 1910), 697–713.

[15]This group of writing includes: *The Organization of Ocean Commerce* (Philadelphia: The University of Pennsylvania, 1905); *The Ocean Carrier* (New York: G. P. Putnam's Sons, 1908); "Ocean Freight Rates," *Political Science Quarterly*, XXI (June, 1906), 237–63; "Ocean Freight Rates and Their Control by Line Carriers," *Journal of Political Economy*, XIV (November, 1906), 525-41; "The World Carriers and the Panama Canal," *Journal of Geography*, XI (March, 1913), 227–31.

[16]J. Russell Smith, *Industrial and Commercial Geography* (New York: Henry Holt and Co., 1913), pp. 734–959.

the fact that they incorporated one of the most careful, accurate, and minute analyses of overseas ommerce extent at the time.

The third group of writings[17] in this early period was the most significant. They, too, were largely inspired by Smith's work on the Isthmian Canal Commission. Later he also used them in *Industrial and Commercial Geography*. In these articles an emerging power of regional, economic analysis was evident. Charles C. Colby, in his discussion of the development of geography, made direct reference to "The Economic Geography of the Argentine Republic" as setting a high standard for the regional, type-study approach it heralded.[18]

All the articles of the third group gave attention to existing economic conditions, the factors underlying them, and the possibilities for solving economic problems by improving old and building new industries. Increasingly, they placed emphasis upon causes, relationships, and meanings, rather than upon statistics and descriptive facts. Furthermore, Smith's vision of the use of modern technology to turn tropical wastelands into productive regions was far ahead of his time.

[17]This series of writings includes: "Western South America and Its Relations to American Trade," *Annals of the American Academy of Political and Social Science*, XVIII (November, 1901), 446–67; "The Economic Geography of the Argentine Republic," *Bulletin of the American Geographical Society*, XXXV (February, 1903), 130–43; "The Economic Geography of Chile," *Bulletin of the American Geographical Society*, XXXVI (January, 1904), 1–15; "The Economic Importance of the Plateaux in Tropic America," *Bulletin of the American Geographical Society*, XXXVII (August, 1905), 461–68; "The Intercontinental Railroad," *North American Review*, CLXXXV (June, 1907), 283–92; "Economic Geography and Its Relation to Economic Theory and Higher Education," *Bulletin of the American Geographical Society*, XXXIX (August, 1907), 472–82.

[18]Charles C. Colby, "Changing Currents of Geographic Thought in America," *Annals of the Association of American Geographers*, XXVI (March, 1936), 22.

An important article in the third group illustrated Smith's growth in geographic understanding and, in particular, his evolving concept of economic geography. It stated:

Economic geography cannot stop with a mere enumeration of the physical resources. There may be conditions present that bar the way to their utilization, and resources are resources only in the light of their prospective or possible conversions into utilities available for human consumption. Natural resources and man must both be considered.[17]

Thus, in comparison with the two earlier groups of writings, the last exhibited his increased insight into the nature of geography. These later articles were broader in scope, more mature in concept, and portrayed a definite feeling for the human element. They also applied geographic principles to the utilization of resources. All these elements pointed the way to Smith's development of the concept of human-use geography around which he organized *Industrial and Commercial Geography* and most of his other books.

These articles also showed that Smith, like his contemporaries, was seeking a definition for the new science of geography, and in so doing, faced the same problems and made the same errors. An article that illustrated his early, somewhat confused search for geographic meaning was "Economic Geography and Its Relation to Economic Theory and Higher Education." This writing was a composite of the various aspects of Smith's thinking at the time. In keeping with the temper of the period, Smith's early, somewhat deterministic, tendency was evident. He

[19]J. Russell Smith, "The Economic Geography of Chile," *Bulletin of the American Geographical Society*, XXXVI (January, 1904), 3.

48 J. RUSSELL SMITH

stated very specifically that Darwin's theory of evolution
had paved the way for modern geography, in that it
demonstrated that organisms were largely shaped by their
surroundings. Accordingly, life progressed mechanically
by organic responses to environmental changes. Smith believed that: "We have received from nineteenth-century
biology the sweeping truth that organisms are what their
environment has made them. . . . Just how much it means
for man, for races, and for civilization, we have only begun
to realize." [20]

In the same article was his apparently contradictory
statement of the importance of the human element in the
relationship between earth and man. Here, Smith first
expressed the concept of human use in organized form
when he stated: "Economic geography is the description
and interpretation of lands in terms of their usefulness to
humanity. Its net result is the understanding of the relation between the people of a district and their physical
environment. . . ." [21] Accordingly, he believed that, "for
the great mass of humanity the geography that is to be of
interest will have primarily the human interest. . . ." [22]
Smith's dichotomy in thinking was gradually dispelled
and the concept of human use became the dominant
theme in his subsequent writings.

Smith's adoption of the concept of human use as the
focus of economic geography brought immediate comments from other geographers. Tower's were highly pertinent. In his important essay, "Scientific Geography: The
Relation of Its Contents to its Subdivisions," where he
attempted to give organization to geographic material,
Tower said of Smith's theory:

[20]Smith, "Economic Geography and Its Relation to Economic Theory
and Higher Education," p. 474.
[21]*Ibid.*, p. 475.
[22]*Ibid.*, p. 473.

A definition of economic geography which does fall in line with the scientific concept of geography is found in the brief, but effective, statements, that "economic geography is the description and interpretation of lands in terms of their usefulness to humanity." . . . This definition alone makes possible a broad concept of economic geography, since it minimizes the narrow idea of actual use. The question of "the usefulness to humanity" is a thing quite apart from the mere consideration of application of material, etc.

Economic geography, according to this concept, stands first, and most important, of the subdivisions under the head of anthropogeography, as furnishing an estimate of the varied physical foundations on which man has risen above the savage animal and based his upward course in civilization.[23]

Such comments were indicative of the regard which many prominent geographers had for Smith because of his work in human geography and his attempts to formulate an organizing concept for the field.

For the next six years, except for the publication of *The Ocean Carrier*, which in content really belonged to his early commercial period, and several articles on conservation and agriculture, Smith devoted most of his energies to his first major work, *Industrial and Commercial Geograhpy*, which served as a framework for presenting the evolving concept of human use.

Early Textbooks in Commercial Geography

Textbook writing had not kept pace with the changing content and meaning of geography. The dearth of material in the field forced Smith to rely on the first ten

[23]Walter Sheldon Tower, "Scientific Geography: The Relation of Its Contents to Its Subdivisions," *Bulletin of the American Geographical Society*, XLII (November, 1913), 817–18.

monographs of the National Geographic Society,[24] Tarr's *Elementary Physical Geography*,[25] and Chisholm's *Handbook of Commercial Geography*[26] for reading material for his students in commerce and industry. He also made occasional use of various commercial geographies extant at the time.[27] All these works, however, were inadquate either because of their heavy physical slant or their purely descriptive and statistical approach. None was really in keeping with the trend toward human-economic geography based on the analysis of the underlying relationships between the physical environment and man's economic activities and resource utilization. Because of the lack of an adequate text, Smith was prompted to write *Industrial and Commercial Geography*.[28]

That this book helped fulfill the need for a modern economic geography text was borne out by comments on the work. Charles C. Colby, in his 1935 presidential address before the Association of American Geographers, hailed it as heralding a great awakening of interest in the field of economic geography: "This notable volume provided an organization and a content for courses at the college level and stimulated much thinking and research in the field. Seldom has a textbook had wider influence." [29]

[24]*National Geographic Monographs,* I–X (New York: American Book Company, 1895). These were prepared under the auspices of the National Geographic Society. The monographs dealt chiefly with the geology and physical geography of the United States.

[25]Ralph S. Tarr, *Elementary Physical Geography* (New York: Macmillan and Co., 1896).

[26]George G. Chisholm, *Handbook of Commercial Geography* (London: Longmans, Green and Co., 1890).

[27]Reference is made to commercial geographies by the following authors: Trotter, 1903; Redway, 1903; Gannett, Garrison, and Houston, 1905; Robinson, 1910; Gregory, Keller, and Bishop, 1910; Brigham, 1911.

[28]Interview with Professor Smith, July 13, 1953.

[29]Colby, "Changing Currents of Geographic Thought in America," pp. 22–23.

Lester E. Klimm, a well-known geographer and former student of Smith, had this to say: "It was probably the first true American college text on the subject."[30]

Isaiah Bowman, writing in 1925, stated that one of the main objectives of economic and commercial geography was "to interpret the earth in terms of its usefulness to humanity, as J. Russell Smith sets the problem in *Industrial and Commercial Geography*." [31] Bowman further stated that Smith's book was still the leading American text, in which economic theory and the problems of trade, transportation, and industrial development were interwoven with the elements of the physical environment.[32] The first book that might in any way have been called a rival was Whitbeck and Finch's *Economic Geography*,[33] published eleven years later. *Industrial and Commercial Geography* has consistently outsold competitors, however, and is still one of the leaders in the field.[34]

What prompted this praise from the other geographers? To a certain extent, the foregoing comments pointed out the book's main virtues. However, a more detailed study of *Industrial and Commercial Geography* is necessary to fully illustrate its significance and meaning.

Analysis of Industrial and Commercial Geography

Primarily, *Industrial and Commercial Geography* pre-

[30]Interview with Professor Lester E. Klimm, Professor of Geography at the Wharton School of Finance and Commerce of the University of Pennsylvania, July 17, 1957.

[31]Bowman, "Commercial Geography as a Science, Reflections on Some Recent Books," p. 285.

[32]Bowman, "Commercial Geography as a Science, Reflections on Some Recent Books," p. 291.

[33]Ray H. Whitback and V. C. Finch, *Economic Geography* (New York: McGraw–Hill Book Company, Inc., 1924).

[34]Interview with Charles A. Madison, editor of the college textbook division of Henry Holt and Company, June 15, 1959.

sented in fully developed book form Smith's human-use theory as applied to economic geography. Smith stated in the preface to *Industrial and Commercial Geography:*

This book aims to interpret the earth in terms of its usefulness to humanity. Since the primary interest is humanity rather than parts of the earth's surface, the book deals with human activities as affected by the earth, rather than with parts of the earth as they affect human activities.[35]

This statement and many others in the text resolved the dichotomy in thinking exhibited by the 1907 article.[36] Six years later, man rather than the natural environment was much more definitely the dominating force, since the main aim of geography was to aid man in commanding the earth instead of being controlled by nature. Geographic influence replaced geographic response and organic factors became coordinate with the physical landscape.[37] Thus, it was apparent that by 1913, Smith had made his decision in favor of the human focus.

In writing his first major work, Smith acknowledged the influence of such Americans as Shaler, Davis, Tower, Brigham, Bowman, and Huntington, as well as of European geographers. For example, in reference to Tower, Smith said in the preface to the book: "In the preparation of this book, I am greatly indebted to Professor Walter S. Tower, of Chicago. It is impossible for me to estimate the influence that he has had upon it through the years of friendly conference and cogent criticism."[38]

The book was divided into two parts, the first entitled

[35]Smith, *Industrial and Commercial Geography,* 1913, p. v.
[36]Smith, "Economic Geography and Its Relation to Economic Theory and Higher Education," 473–75.
[37]Brigham, "The Organic Side of Geography: Its Nature and Its Limits," 422–43.
[38]Smith, *Industrial and Commercial Geography,* 1913, pp. v–vi.

"Industrial Geography," and the second, "Commercial Geography." From the standpoint of the meaning of geography, the first chapter, entitled "Our Changing Environment," was the most significant. Here, the keynote was the importance of the environment to man as well as man's increasing control and use of nature through technological advance. Smith constantly pointed out that technology helped to develop and interrelate the whole world and to equalize differences between areas. Taking transportation and commerce as examples, Smith emphasized that:

The environment of mankind is undergoing the greatest and most sudden revolution that it has ever experienced. It is the change from the local environment, in which the local conditions dominated, to the world environment to which one export commodity admits us and which tends to make us all alike.

This world environment creates a world commerce and a world market which we must understand before we fully comprehend man's relation to any community. . . . This possible separation of the sustenance space from the home space has come almost entirely within the past hundred years, chiefly through the assistance of coal and iron working together in the form of the steam engine.[39]

Thus, in the transitional phase of his career, Smith had developed a dynamic view of man in relation to his earth, an earth which was rapidly being modified through science. It was partly this acute awareness of the human factor and its implications that distinguished *Industrial and Commercial Geography* from previous texts in the field.

The text was further unique in its emphasis on the

[39]Smith, *Industrial and Commercial Geography*, 1913, pp. 15–16.

importance of climate in man's environment. Smith was the first author of a text in economic geography to fully incorporate the climatic factor as a basic element of the physical world and to place climate on a plane equal to physiography, which had previously dominated texts. Smith did not do original work in climatology as such. He was strongly influenced by Ellsworth T. Huntington's work in climatology.[40] Because of his admiration for Huntington, Smith was chosen to give the honorary address when Huntington was awarded the Kane Gold Medal of the Geographical Society of Philadelphia for outstanding work in the field. As Smith indicated in this address: "Dr. Huntington is doing what I regard as the most important geographical work now being carried on by any individual."[41]

In the vein of Huntington, Smith stated in *Industrial and Commercial Geography*:

Civilization is a product of adversity. The great civilizations of all time seem to have arisen where nature made production possible only a part of the year, and thus made it necessary for man to work and save up for a time when he could not produce. . . . Accordingly, there has been no great civilization in the warm, moist parts of the torrid zone, where nature does the most to make easy the support of life. . . .

This abundance without effort does not require or induce the work habit. For this reason lands of perennial plenty

[40]Ellsworth T. Huntington was among the leaders in the United States in the early study of climatology and the influence of climate on cultural patterns. Some of his most pertinent works are: *The Pulse of Asia* (Boston: Houghton, Mifflin and Company, 1907); *Civilization and Climate* (New Haven: Yale University Press, 1915); *World Power and Evolution* (New Haven: Yale University Press, 1919).

[41]J. Russell Smith, "Ellsworth Huntington, Geographer," *Bulletin of the Geographical Society of Philadelphia*, XIV (January, 1916), 21.

have never been lands of power. . . . If fruitful harvest is followed by the stimulus of frost we have the best conditions for the development of energetic races.[42]

Thus, Smith gave full play to the climatic factor in shaping civilization. At the same time, the above and similar statements showed elements of climatic determinism. This determinism was also apparent in the works of Huntington and other workers in the field; but, one cannot judge too severely during this early period. The field was too new and the ground too uncertain to expect present day insights. Although the weight on climatic influence was rather heavy, it broadened the scope of geography and this, in itself, was an important development. Time would temper Smith's conclusions as it did those of Huntington.[43]

Other new, dynamic elements of human geography that were exhibited in Part I of *Industrial and Commercial Geography* were the emphasis on the creation of new industries through the application of modern technology and attention to wise utilization of natural resources. The last chapter, "The Expansion of Industry and Resources," gave a good analysis of both these elements which are essential for national and international growth and development. In the stream of human use, Smith defined a resource as "something which may be turned into, or made to produce, a useful commodity, and thus give rise

[42]Smith, *Industrial and Commercial Geography*, 1913, pp. 5–7.

[43]In his earlier works such as *Civilization and Climate and The Pulse of Asia*, Huntington concluded that climatic influences are perhaps the most important in man's environment and that a favorable climate was almost essential to a higher civilization. In later analyzing exceptions to this theory, especially in relation to Iceland and parts of China, Huntington modified his earlier position and included other factors such as selective migration as important in cultural evolution. This modification is evident in Huntington's *The Character of Races* (New York: Charles Scribner's Sons, 1924).

to an object of consumption or of commerce, and aid in the support of population." [44]

Smith considered science, positively used, as the medium through which man could produce an ever-broadening range of useful commodities and render productive underdeveloped parts of the earth. Scientific planning was his answer to the then current cry that America's chances for progress and prosperity were diminishing. Smith felt that negative thinking was not founded on geographic or scientific fact, but, rather, was "due to the shortcomings of our financial and industrial system, and from our . . . purely irrational method of distributing wealth and holding property." [45] Here Smith was speaking as a "possibilist" as well as a critic of aspects of our economic system. His words presented a liberal social and economic outlook that, at the time, was rather unique in a text.

In the remaining chapters of Part I, Smith proceeded to a detailed analysis of the various agricultural, manufacturing, and mining industries. Again, he pointed out the future potential of underdeveloped areas of the world, especially the tropical regions, which were of lifelong interest to him.

Part II of the book, entitled "Commercial Geography," was partly derived from materials in *The Organization of Ocean Commerce, The Ocean Carrier,* and Smith's early articles on trade. Although the second section was not as important as the first, it was significant because here Smith attempted to formulate laws of trade based on differences in cultural-economic patterns and levels of industrial development. At the same time, he gave a good delineation of the trade routes of the world which

[44]Smith, *Industrial and Commercial Geography*, 1913, p. 640.
[45]Smith, *Industrial and Commercial Geography*, 1913, p. 640.

rivals similar treatments of today. Geographic factors were applied as a basis of analysis, and attention was given to possible changes which might result from technological advances.

Many of the specific points he made have become dated because of the time factor. Those rooted in basic geographic and economic principles, however, were of lasting value. So, too, were those which showed an appreciation of the importance of commerce in developing and maintaining national strength, independence, and world cooperation.

Probably the most important thinking in the second section was in his final chapter, "The Influence of Geographic Factors On The Commercial Policy of Nations."[46] Here he pointed out in detail that a nation achieved independence and greatness only when it acquired freedom in government and a self-supporting network of industries linked with a world-wide, mutually cooperative commercial pattern.[47] The theme of international economic cooperation as a foundation of world peace was a constant one with Smith. The attempt now being made at currency and trade revision to facilitate a common market in Western Europe is in line with suggestions that Smith made in the second decade of the century. Western Europe may at last have awakened to the reality that peace and prosperity can be obtained only through mutual aid and cooperation instead of trade barriers that, in the past, as Smith pointed out, inevitably led to war.

Summary

The chief importance of *Industrial and Commercial*

[46]Smith, *Industrial and Commercial Geography*, 1913, pp. 920–33.
[47]*Ibid.*, pp. 892–98.

Geography was its role in initiating a new era in geography textbook writing characterized by the organization of material around the relationship between physical factors and human-economic patterns. Smith employed the concept of human use as his organizing central theme. This concept was not strictly Smith's invention. It was partly derived from such varied sources as the human-geographic writings of Herbertson and Shaler. In his use of climate as a prime geographical control in delimiting natural regions with distinctive human-use patterns, he was strongly influenced by the studies of Wladimir Köeppen of Germany, Unstead and Taylor of Great Briain, and Huntington in the United States.[48] Smith did creative work, however, by being the first to fully organize economic activities into a regional pattern around the theme of human use and to apply this method to textbook writing.

Then, too, *Industrial and Commercial Geography,* though still showing signs of determinism, also exhibited many aspects of a more modern and possibilistic approach. This was evidenced not only by Smith's elaboration of the theory of human use, but also by his prophetic and dynamic emphasis on the changes that man can bring to the world through technology and world cooperation. Significant, also, was Smith's role in broadening the content base of geography to include climatology as well as landforms in the study of the natural environment. All these elements in *Industrial and Commercial Geography* showed how his interests had broadened from the early days of 1899–1901 when his main focus was the Panama Canal.

[48]J. Russell Smith, "The Use of Type Studies in Elementary Geography." Unpublished article dated October 6, 1928.

The book was important, too, in displaying Smith's growing proficiency in writing. His material, though filled with facts, was centered around ideas and was written in a simple, interesting manner, supplemented by well-captioned graphs, charts, maps, and pictures. The progress made is evident when this 1913 text is contrasted with his first book, *The Organization of Ocean Commerce.* *Industrial and Commercial Geography* marked the development of Smith's mature style which, by its dynamic quality, readability, and interesting presentation, contributed to the large circulation of his books.

The later editions of 1925, 1946,[49] and 1955[50] were significant because they showed the growing influence of the French possibilistic school, the modification of the previous overtones of climatic determinism, and the emphasis on world economic cooperation. In these revisions, Smith was increasingly aware of the role of geography as a dynamic science. The books also reflected the deepened insight of a mature man who had passed through the tormented era of world war. Smith pointed out sadly that man's inability to live together on an international level restricted the progress that modern technology offered to the world. As he said: "Man's apparent inability to solve the problems of war and human poverty is perhaps the greatest tragedy in world history. Perhaps these are the supreme cultural lags." [51] He indicated very succinctly the challenge of modern times: "We stand on the threshold of the golden age of material and comfort, or per-

[49]J. Russell Smith and M. Ogden Phillips, *Industrial and Commercial Geography* (New York: Henry Holt and Company, 1946).

[50]J. Russell Smith, M. Ogden Phillips, and Thomas R. Smith, *Industrial and Commercial Geography* (New York: Henry Holt and Company, 1955). Thomas R. Smith is one of Smith's sons and a professor of geography at the University of Kansas.

[51]Smith and Phillips, *Industrial and Commercial Geography,* p. 8.

haps we are standing on the brink of crashing, calamitous destruction. Which? That depends upon ourselves." [52] In conclusion, Smith said:

The major problem facing the generation that reads this book is not the control of natural resources. It is the control of the human spirit residing in men with science in their heads. Our material possessions are as nothing; moral values are suddenly become the overpowering reality.[53]

His attitude epitomized the growth of geography from the study of purely physical factors to that of man's relations not only with the earth but also with his fellow men, in terms of world citizenship and cooperation. Viewed in this light, Smith believed that geography had begun to fulfill its function as the bridge between the natural and the social sciences.

SMITH'S CONTRIBUTION TO THE DEVELOPMENT OF REGIONAL GEOGRAPHY

Smith's major work in the field of regional, human-economic geography on the advanced level was *North America*.[54] Just as he helped meet a need in general human-economic geography by writing *Industrial and Commercial Geography*, so also he filled the vacuum in regional geography by writing *North America*.

Recognition of the Need for a Regional Geography of North America

[52]*Ibid.*, p. 932.
[53]*Ibid.*, p. 957.
[54]J. Russell Smith, *North America* (New York: Harcourt, Brace and Co., 1925).

Roorbach's 1914 report singled out the pressing need for a detailed regional study of North America. Roorbach quoted W. L. G. Joerg as saying:

In my opinion, our greatest need is a systematic geography of the United States, or preferably, of North America, along modern lines, similar in scope to Mackinder's *Britain and the British Seas*, Partsch's *Mitteleuropa*, and Vidal de la Blache's, *La France: Tableau Géographique*. It should, of course, embrace all phases of the subject, both physical and human, and be sufficiently detailed to bring out all essentials. At present we have no such works in English. Those available are either out of date or ungeographical in point of view, or, where this is not the case, do not present all phases of the subject.[55]

Other contemporary writers showed similar realization of the need for a new regional treatment of North America. Their agreement pointed up the growing recognition of the region as the culmination of geographic method. As early as the first years of the twentieth century, Tower, Brigham, Davis, and others were writing of the basic role of the region. Tower's statement in 1906 was prophetic in pointing out that in regional geography "lies the direction for the future advance in geography."[56] Nevin M. Fenneman, Mark Jefferson, and W. L. G. Joerg contributed strongly to the stream of development by their various delineations of the natural regions of North America.[57]

[55]Roorbach, "The Trend of Modern Geography, A Symposium," p. 808.
[56]Tower, "A Field for Studies in Regional Geography," p. 484.   ;
[57]Reference is made to the following: Nevin M. Fenneman, "The Circumference of Geography," *Annals of the Association of American Geographers*, IX (1919), 3–11; Nevin M. Fenneman, "Physiographic Divisions of the United States," *Annals of the Association of American Geographers*, VI (1916), 19–98; Mark Jefferson, "Some Considerations on the Geographical Provinces of the United States," *Annals of the As-*

European Regional Geographic Studies

In tracing the development of regional geography, initial attenion must be focused on Europe where the regional concept originated. Although elements of regional geography were present in the works of Alexander von Humboldt, Karl Ritter, and Friedrich Ratzel, the real impetus to the movement came at the beginning of the twentieth century. In all principal European centers of geographic thought, the region was conceived of as a key subject for both technical and empirical study. Vidal de la Blache, dean of French geographers, set the pace in his *La France: Tableau Géographique,* and, together with his famed pupils, Jean Brunhes and Lucien Gallois, encouraged students to write monographs on the regions of France.

In Germany, Alfred Hettner[58] led the way in stating the nature and importance of regional organization in geography. His lead was soon followed by other German geographers, notably Siegfried Passarge.[59]

Among British publications were the relevant sections in Herbertson's "The Major Natural Regions: An Essay in Systematic Geography." [60] In his approach, however, Herbertson was more interested in natural rather than cultural divisions. Greater attention was given to the cultural region by Percy M. Roxby and John F. Unstead.[61]

sociation of American Geographers, VII (1917), 2–16; Wolfgang L. G. Joerg, "The Subdivision of North America into Natural Regions: A Preliminary Inquiry," *Annals of the Association of American Geographers,* IV (1914), 55–83.

[58]Richard Hartshorne, *The Nature of Geography,* Prepared for the Association of American Geographers (Lancaster, Pa.: The Science Printing Press Company, 4th printing, 1951), pp. 138–40, 305–11.

[59]*Ibid.,* pp. 315–19.

[60]Andrew J. Herbertson, "The Major Natural Regions: An Essay in Systematic Geography," *Geographical Journal,* XXV (1905), 300–12.

[61]Hartshorne, *The Nature of Geography,* pp. 100, 257, 293–94.

In 1924, Llewellyn Jones' and Patrick Bryan's *North America*[62] appeared. This work was of true scientific calibre and the first English regional study from the point of view of modern geography.

American Contributions to the Regional Geography of North America

Because of the early dominance of physiography in America, the majority of our beginning regional treatments were in terms of natural regions. Nathaniel Southgate Shaler, social philosopher as well as dynamic geologist, was the American pioneer in writing a regional geography of North America that emphasized human and cultural factors. His accomplishment was evident in *Nature and Man in America* (1891)[63] and *The Story of Our Continent* (1894),[64] the latter for use in the schools.

Another important treatment of North America was given in *The United States of America* (1894),[65] produced under Shaler's editorship. Shaler's work demonstrated why he is considered one of the earliest American geographers to realize the importance of the regional approach in both its human and physical aspects. Smith, among others, acknowledge his indebtedness to Shaler, calling him "my unseen master" and "a pioneer appreciator of the relationship between earth and man." [66] Concluding his acknowledgment to Shaler in *North America*, Smith expressed

[62]Llewellyn R. Jones and Patrick W. Bryan, *North America* (London: Methuen & Co., Ltd., 1924).

[63]Nathaniel S. Shaler, *Nature and Man in America* (New York: C. Scribner's Sons, 1891).

[64]Nathaniel S. Shaler, *The Story of Our Continent* (Boston: Ginn & Compay, 1894).

[65]Nathaniel S. Shaler, ed., *The United States of America* (New York: D. Appleton & Co., 1894).

[66]Smith, *North America*, p. vi.

hope that his book would manifest Shaler's viewpoint to a later generation that Shaler could not teach in person.[67] After Shaler, regional geography slipped back to the predominant theme of the time, that of physiography. Geographers were not as yet fully prepared to follow his more modern insight.

The versatile and energetic William Morris Davis also played a role in developing regional physical geography through his chapters on the United States and North America in John Stuart Mills's *International Geography*[68] His work helped transform general physiography into geographic material through the use of the regional principle.

In 1911 regional geography came fully into its own with the publication of Bowman's *Forest Physiography*,[69] in which the body of geological literature, including that of the United States Geological Society, was summarized and set forth regionally. It is usually considered the first adequate statement of the regional principle in an American work on physiography.[70]

Smith's Work in Regional Geography

Smith's main contribution to regional geography came through *North America*, which furthered the approach initiated by Shaler—that of developing the human aspects of the region, as against the purely physical. As W. L. G. Joerg pointed out, it was not until eleven years after

[67]Smith, *North America*, p. vi.

[68]Wolfgang L. G. Joerg, "The Geography of North America: A History of Its Regional Exposition," *Geographical Review*, XXVI (October, 1936), 643.

[69]Isaiah Bowman, *Forest Physiography* (New York: J. Wiley & Sons, 1911).

[70]Joerg, "The Geography of North America: A History of Its Regional Exposition," 644.

Roorbach's 1914 report, which demonstrated the need for a regional geography of North America, that the first modern regional geography of North America by an American appeared in the form of J. Russell Smith's *North America*.[71] Joerg further stated: "Here was an account, organized sufficiently minutely by regions and of sufficient length to deal adequately with all the essentials . . . and written in an interesting and direct manner, often with brilliance." [72]

In the words of Smith's former student, Dr. Lester E. Klimm, the important thing to remember about the significance of Smith's *North America* was that: "Here, for the first time, he presented a regionalization of the continent in terms of the way human beings use it, not the 'natural region,' or the 'physiographic regions,' of his predecessors, but 'human-use regions.' " [73]

In analyzing *North America*, the historical significance of the book is lost if it is evaluated in terms of the accuracy of its human-use organization. While at the time Smith's human-use divisions were in a sense a work of art, they do not fully meet the standards of modern methodology. However, if the book is considered in terms of its being a pioneer attempt at humanizing and systematizing the regional approach, then its true importance in the development of regional human geography is seen.

In *North America*, Smith at once established the themes of the intimate relationship between man and nature and man's increasing ability to modify the earth through tech-

[71]Joerg, "The Geography of North America: A History of Its Regional Exposition," 648.

[72]*Ibid.*

[73]Dr. Lester E. Klimm, in the capacity of Councilor of the American Geographical Society, in an unprinted speech delivered on the presentation of the Cullum Geographical Medal to Professor J. Russell Smith, November 14, 1956.

nology. He also showed growth in awareness of geography's task of educating people in the constructive use of the earth's resources. As he pointed out, the America of 1925 was passing through a period of economic trial with rapidly expanding population, accompanied by an unparalleled waste and destruction of resources. With this reality to face, Smith questioned:

What of the future? This is the concern of every intelligent citizen—a growing concern. It will be even more acutely an affair which the youth now being education must face. Their education should give them a thorough knowledge of the continent on which they are to live. Hence this book.[74]

The necessity of training Americans for wise use of their resources set the pattern for the human-use organization of *North America*. With knowledge of the natural features and potential of regions, people could apply their skill to developing resources and establishing a sound and progressive base for national growth.

In many of the sections dealing with attitudes, Smith's ideas resembled those in Shaler's *Nature and Man in America* and *The United States of America*. Smith, like Shaler, pointed out the importance of geographic factors, especially good land, a wealth of resources, and generally favorable climate, in making America a rich, free land. However, living in the contemporary world, Smith was better able to see the changes wrought by modern science and to comprehend the great waste of natural resources that was insidiously robbing us of part of our national wealth. Therefore, throughout his detailed delineation of the forty-four areas into which he divided North America, he again stressed the conservation and scientific develop-

[74]Smith, *North America*, p. iv.

ment of natural resources.

In such chapters as the final one, "The Trade, Place, and Future of North America," [75] his insight into basic problems facing the country and the world reflected today's thinking. He pointed out that the people of the world had been made interdependent by the geography and modern science. People had to awaken to this interdependence and cease building economic and trade barriers and other sources of conflict which carried the seeds of war. Smith stated the problem of the twentieth century very succintly when he said that "Science and invention have given man the powers of Classic Gods," [76] but had man learned sufficiently well to live with his neighbors on an international basis so as to prevent another world holocaust?[77] He concluded that the future of North America depended upon the course chosen. "We do, indeed, live in a new world and we have given our lives as hostages to its continuance . . . a dangerous world in which to live, as well as a wonderful world." [78]

Other editions of *North America* were published in 1940 and 1942.[79] Essentially the structure remained the same. The revisions added new and expanded material and refocused the need to bring about a cooperative relationship among nations.

In 1937 Smith wrote *Men and Resources*,[80] also a study of North America and its place in world geography. The book was really a condensation of *North America* for use on the high-school level, just as *Commerce and Industry*

[75]Smith, *North America,* pp. 796–813.

[76]*Ibid.,* p. 809.

[77]*Ibid., pp.* 809–10.

[78]*Ibid.,* p. 807.

[79]J. Russell Smith and M. Ogden Phillips, *North America* (New York: Harcourt, Brace and Co., 1940); 1942.

[80]J. Russell Smith, *Men and Resources* (New York: Harcourt, Brace and Co., 1937).

(1916),[81] was a simplified version of *Industrial and Commercial Geography* for use on the secondary level.

Thus Smith, through his advanced writings, played a significant role in the early development of human, economic, and regional geography. His books, *Industrial and Cmmercial Geography* and *North America*, were the first texts in their respective fields to successfully apply the new approaches in geographic theory and method which came to the fore in the beginning quarter of the twentieth century. By his human-use focus and his belief in world cooperation and scientific progress, Smith aided in placing man in the forefront of geographic study. His work thus facilitated the evolution of geography into a social science geared toward helping man to understand and fulfill his potential in relation to his world.

[81]J. Russell Smith, *Commerce and Industry* (New York: Henry Holt and Company, 1916).

IV

Smith's Work at the Wharton School of Finance and Commerce

GEOGRAPHY DID NOT ORIGINATE WITH SMITH AT THE UNIVERSITY of Pennsylvania; rather initial credit must be given to his professor, the late Emory R. Johnson, economist, Professor of Commerce and Transportation and, later, Dean of the Wharton School, who had been doing work in geography since the early 1890's.

THE BEGINNINGS OF GEOGRAPHY AT WHARTON

Johnson, a versatile and dynamic teacher, played an influential role in Smith's formative development. In addition to personality, Smith resembled Johnson in background and training. Both were farm boys with a deep interest in the land; both had taught secondary school to finance their university work; both had undergraduate training in history and economics.

In 1893, after receiving his doctorate in economics from

the University of Pennsylvania, Johnson was appointed lecturer in the Department of Economics and Social Science of the Wharton School to teach "Transportation," [1] his field of specialization. By 1896, Johnson had advanced to be Assistant Professor of Transportation and Commerce and was teaching two additional new courses, "The Theory and Geography of Commerce" and "Physical and Economic Geography."[2] The attention given to geography in both these courses showed the significance that Johnson attached to the subject in shedding light on man's economic activities. As he once told a now noted geographer and former graduate of the Wharton School, "I studied and taught geography because I couldn't study and teach commerce without it." [3]

These two new courses were particularly significant because, other than the work of Shaler at Harvard, they were the first courses in any American university that actually warranted being called human-economic geography. William Morris Davis confirmed this judgment by this statement: "The chief impulse toward the higher study of economic and commercial aspects of geography in America appears to have come, about 1900, from the Wharton School of Finance and Commerce, in the University of Pennsylvania." [4] From this beginning at the Wharton School, human geography, through its economic aspects, was to see a development parallel to the simultaneous

[1] Interview with Dr. Lester E. Klimm, Professor of Geography at the Wharton School of Finance and Commerce of the University of Pennsylvania, July 17, 1957.

[2] *Catalogue of the University of Pennsylvania*, 1896–97 (Philadelphia: Published by the University, December, 1896), pp. 77–78.

[3] Interview with Dr. Lester E. Klimm, July 17, 1957.

[4] William Morris Davis, "The Progress of Geography in the United States," *Annals of the Association of American Geographers*, XIV (December, 1924), 201. See also Wolfgang L. G. Joerg, "The Geography of North America: A History of its Regional Exposition," *Geographical Review*, XXVI (October, 1936), 642.

growth of physical geography at Harvard under Davis.[5]

Credit for the early development of geography at Wharton must also go to the pioneering character of the Wharton School. Established in 1881, it was the first division of an American university to offer a four-year course in finance and commerce. Its benefactor, Joseph Wharton, a wealthy Philadelphia lawyer and businessman, stipulated that the school should train students for careers in civil government and business.[6]

In order to realize the objectives of a broad cultural background coupled with specialization, courses were established in both academic and business subjects. Such famous figures in American history and letters as John B. McMaster, Edward P. Cheyney, and James Harvey Robinson gave courses at Wharton as well as at the University of Pennsylvania proper. The course in Finance and Economy covered four years and led to the degree of Bachelor of Science in Economics.[7] The conditions for admission were identical with those required by the division of Arts and Sciences and graduate degrees in political economy were offered under the auspices of the Department of Philosophy.

The plan of instruction was both liberal and practical, embracing recitations, lectures, seminars, and field work. The main endeavor was to train students "to think independently and to exclude all dogmatism in political and economic teaching.[8] Experimentation was encouraged and

[5]Joerg, "The Geography of North America: A History of Its Regional Exposition," 642.

[6]First Annual Report of the Wharton School of Finance and Economy, University of Pennsylvania, May 1, 1884, p. 11.

[7]In 1894, when the first courses in geography were introduced at Wharton, Smith was a freshman enrolled in the four-year course in Finance and Economy.

[8]First Annual Report of the Wharton School of Finance and Economy, 1884, p. 9.

original research, under the direction of the professors, was an integral part of a student's training.

Geography Comes Into Its Own

After Johnson's work on the Isthmian Canal Commission, his courses underwent an interesting expansion and reorientation.[9] Prompted by the belief that students of economics and finance needed a basic knowledge of geography, he placed a deepened emphasis in his courses on the geographic factors underlying American commerce and industry. In order to have specific course work in physiography and economic geography, Johnson chose J. Paul Goode in 1901 as his assistant. Goode not only held a doctorate in economic geography,[10] but also had a background in physical geography. His interest and training were evident from the work he offered in physiography, climatology, geology, and economic and political geography.[11]

Now that he had a specialist to take over for him, Johnson felt free to relinquish the teaching of geography and to devote full time to his own fields of commerce and transportation.[12] The new treatment of geography and commerce as separate specializations foreshadowed

[9]For a detailed listing and description of the new courses see: *Catalogue of the University of Pennsylvania,* 1901–02, pp. 92–96.

[10]Goode received his doctorate under Johnson in 1901.

[11]*Catalogue of the University of Pennsylvania,* 1901-02, p. 151; *Catalogue of the University of Pennsylvania,* 1902–03, pp. 136–37. In 1901–02, Goode was teaching "Physiography" and "Economic Geography of America." In 1902–03, "Physiography" was dropped and, in its place, "Geomorphy, with Economic Applications" and "Climatology with Economic Applications" were given. In the same year he was also offering "Political Geography" in addition to "Economic Geography of America."

[12]Emory R. Johnson, *Life of a University Professor: An Autobiography* (Philadelphia: The University of Pennsylvania, 1931), p. 63.

the future development within the department and
pointed the way to the establishment of geography as a
recognized subject in itself.[13]

Smith's First Year

When Goode left the Wharton School in 1903, Johnson
chose Smith to take his place. Accordingly, the geography
courses were modified to be more in line with Smith's
background, which was rather meager in physical geography. Smith taught three undergraduate courses in his
beginning year. Physiography and climatology were
recombined in a course entitled "Geography and Climatology with Economic Applications."[14] Although consideration was given to the physical aspects of the
environment, Smith stressed the economic applications.
Later, when the department had grown sufficiently, Smith
turned over the work in physical geography to assistants.

The second undergraduate course Smith taught was
"Organization of International Commerce." [15] This was a
course especially tailored for Smith, since it was the subject of his doctoral thesis and closely related to his work
with the Isthmian Canal Commission and his field study
of the leading port cities of Western Europe. In fact, after
1905, the text for the course was his published thesis, *The
Organization of Ocean Commerce*.[16] Smith's interest in

[13]This development was further pointed up by the establishment in
1901 of the subdivision "Geography and Commerce," within the division of Economics and Social Science.

[14]*Catalogue of the University of Pennsylvania*, 1903–04, p. 141.

[15]*Ibid.*, p. 142.

[16]*Supra*, Chap. II, pp. 36–37. In connection with the development of
the course, Smith wrote numerous articles in the field, as well as *The
Ocean Carrier*, and incorporated much of the material of the course
into *Industrial and Commercial Geography*.

international trade was a lasting one and while other
courses came and went, this one was given consistently
during Smith's tenure at Wharton, on both the undergraduate and graduate levels.

"Commercial and Economic Geography," [17] the third
undergraduate course that Smith taught, pointed the way
to the future development of the department along the
lines of human-economic geography. Though not introduced until the evening session of 1905–06, another
course, "Industrial Management," [18] and subsequent related ones, designed especially for those interested in business administration, were also significant in pointing up
another group of courses developed by Smith.

Thus, from Smith's first years at Wharton, two broad
and interrelated areas were crystallizing which epitomized
the basis of his contributions to the development of course
work at Pennsylvania. These areas were human-economic
geography, through the focus of its industrial and commercial aspects, and industrial management.

SMITH'S WORK IN HUMAN-ECONOMIC GEOGRAPHY

AND INDUSTRIAL MANAGEMENT

Human-Economic Geography

In 1906, as a newly promoted assistant professor, "Geography" and "Industry" [19] were united under Smith's leadership as a separate subdivision within the Department of
Economics and Social Science. Thus, geography, which
had started as an offshoot of transportation under Johnson,

[17]*Catalogue of the University of Pennsylvania*, 1903–04, p. 142.
[18]*Ibid.*, 1905–06, p. 212.
[19]*Ibid.*, 1906–07, p. 35.

early became a fully recognized subject under Smith. The department of "Geography and Industry" at Wharton can correctly be termed his creation, and to the new subdivision he gave form, shape, meaning, imagination, and personnel.[20]

Two general tendencies soon became evident in Smith's developing courses just as they did in his writings that grew from the courses and, in turn, stimulated them. These were the increasingly human-geographic nature of the material and the broadening of the scope of human geography. These tendencies can be seen by comparing Smith's courses with those of Johnson and Goode. For example, Smith's course, "Commercial and Economic Geography," was at first largely a reshaping of Johnson's "Commercial Geography" and "American Commerce and Commercial Relations" and Goode's "Economic Geography of America." Johnson's courses, however, had a primarily economic or commercial focus. They were more or less a geography of commerce presented by an economist with an appreciation of geography. In contradistinction, following Goode's abortive lead, Smith gradually progressed towards a true human-economic geography. The change in texts from those of Ralph S. Tarr and George G. Chisholm to Smith's own works made more concrete the new emphasis of the courses.[21]

Smith's course, "Commercial and Economic Geography,"[22] spawned innumerable progeny. Starting in 1903–04 as a broad survey of the natural resources and industries of the United States, the courses that developed

[20]Interview with Dr. Joseph H. Willits, in charge of the Educational Survey of the University of Pennsylvania, and one of Professor Smith's former students, May 18, 1959.
[21]Supra, Chap. II, pp. 41–42.
[22]Catalogue of the University of Pennsylvania, 1903–04, p. 142.

from it gave detailed, analytical attention to all phases of American and foreign economies, including resources, industry, agriculture, and commercial relations. Particularly significant was "Resources of the United States," [23] which became his basic and best-known course in economic geography at Wharton and a requirement for all freshmen.

Dr. Joseph H. Willits described it as a "honey of a course," [24] which brought to life the dynamic theme of the intimate interrelationship between man and nature. In this course, Smith clearly portrayed the great industrial opportunity of the United States when accompanied by modern technology and a progressive socio-economic philosophy.

Important, too, were the courses in industry which he first developed in 1906–07 under the title "American Industry" [25] and later called "Manufacturing Industries of the United States." [26] Industry after industry was studied, with analysis of the "whys" and "hows" of location, production, marketing, competition, and all other human and natural aspects which are necessary for an understanding of American industrial society and its place within the cultural whole. These courses, and others like them, formed the basis of Smith's work at Wharton and later at Columbia.

From the beginning, Smith linked the theoretical with the practical field study of industries. An excellent example of his applied approach was "Field Work in Industry," [27] a course which became a "must" for the student of business and economic geography. This course, and others like it, attempted to give students a feeling for

[23]*Ibid.*, 1910–11, p. 230.
[24]Interview with Dr. Joseph H. Willits, May 18, 1959.
[25]*Catalogue of the University of Pennsylvania*, 1906–07, p. 217.
[26]*Ibid.*, 1910–11, pp. 232–33.
[27]*Ibid.*, 1907–08, p. 255.

the actual conditions in industry by the inspection of shops and factories. Smith used the industrial plants in the Philadelphia area as laboratories for his students. Critical attention was given to the arrangement of plants, transportation facilities, the handling of new material, and the organization of manufacturing. Students made studies of each plant visited and later discussed their findings in seminars. Smith's linking of the practical with the theoretical was one of the essential factors in making his approach alive and meaningful.

By humanizing economic geography, Smith hoped to enable the students to see an economic system as "a segment of society in microcosm."[28] This did not mean that the physical elements were neglected, but rather, that the final focus was primarily on man and his work in keeping with the spirit of modern economic geography. The development of a more modern approach can further be seen in the changing course descriptions, especially after 1906, when, increasingly, countries and industries were studied from the point of view of "a place in which men live and make a living," as described in such courses as "Resources and Agriculture of the United States."[29]

Smith also moved closer to a more modern concept of economic geography, through his use of a regional approach. Like many of his contemporaries, he came to see the importance of the regional idea as the organizing focus of geography.[30] In 1906, he offered "Regional Economic Geography,"[31] in the graduate division, and in the following year, "Economic Conditions in South America"[32] in both the undergraduate and graduate divisions. The

[28]Interview with Dr. Joseph H. Willits, May 18, 1959.
[29]Catalogue of the University of Pennsylvania, 1909–10, p. 273.
[30]Supra, Chap. II, pp. 53–58.
[31]Catalogue of the University of Pennsylvania, 1906–07, p. 312.
[32]Ibid., 1907–08, p. 252.

courses dealing with American and European industries and resources had a similar orientation. Later, a course entitled "The Far East" [33] was introduced. Eventually, what Smith did in his regional approach was to take political divisions of the world, such as countries or continents, and then to present them on the basis of their industrial and commercial patterns. In setting forth these patterns, he analyzed the interrelationship between the physical characteristics of the natural region, such as topography, soil, and climate, and the resultant economic use man made of the natural environment

Smith's use of the region pointed up another important interest of his, the underdeveloped tropical areas of the world. The economic potentialities of these lands, especially in Latin America, was a constant theme in his courses and writings. "Economic Conditions in South America" was a course that was continually being improved throughout Smith's stay at Wharton and was later more fully developed at Columbia. Smith tried to point up the rich investment possibilities in South America for the American Government and private capital. In the course description Smith stated that his objective was to draw attention to the facts of production and trade in this "unappreciated continent," together with a "careful study of the resources and underlying industrial and commercial factors." [34] Smith's early vision of the significance of tropical lands has been more than justified in recent years with the greatly increased importance of tropical regions of Latin America, Africa, the Far East, and the Middle East.

Another evidence of the broadening approach of his

[33]*Ibid.*, 1912–13, p. 205.
[34]*Catalogue of the University of Pennsylvania*, 1907–08, p. 252.

courses was his increased attention to conservation. By 1913 he deemed the subject of such importance that he introduced a course largely devoted to its consideration, entitled "Industrial Resources and Conservation." [35] By this time conservation was also taking a prominent place in his articles and major books.

The extension of the content base of physical geography by the emphasis on the climatic factor also saw realization at the Wharton School. This trend began under Goode, with his treatment of climatology as equal in importance to physiography. Smith continued Goode's attention to the climatic factor. Henceforth, although teaching physical geography for only two years before turning it over to assistants, he continued to emphasize climatic elements in all his subsequent courses and writings.[36]

Smith received help from Walter Sheldon Tower in developing climatology and other aspects of geography at Wharton. Tower became his assistant in 1906 and he taught most of the courses in physical geography. Smith and Tower worked closely together at Wharton and their warm friendship continues to this day. Smith also acknowledged that Tower had some influence on his thinking.[37] During the period that Tower remained at the Wharton School, 1906–1911, he devoted much time to an exploration of the fundamental meaning and content of geography. Both Tower and Smith emphasized the regional approach, the mutual interrelationship between earth and man, and the importance of the climatic factor. With Smith's help and encouragement Tower developed

[35]*Ibid.*, 1913–14, p. 220.
[36]*Supra,* Chap. II, pp. 46–48.
[37]Acknowledgments of Professor Smith to Tower in *Industrial and Commercial Geography,* 1913. Interviews with Smith's former students, Dr. Lester E. Klimm, Dr. Alfred H. Williams, and Dr. Joseph H. Willits.

the basic work in physical geography. Outstanding among
his courses were "Climate and Civilization" [38] and "Earth
and Man." [39]

Rather than belabor the academic question of who
influenced whom, and to what extent, it is more realistic
to say that there was a mutual interaction between Smith
and Tower and that changes in course titles and content
reflected the development of their thinking and that of
their contempories. Tower left Pennsylvania in 1911 to
go to the University of Chicago. His courses were continued by other assistants, among whom were George B.
Roorbach, Joseph H. Willits, and Alfred H. Williams.

INDUSTRIAL MANAGEMENT AND BUSINESS GEOGRAPHY

Since the purpose of the Wharton School was a dual
one, namely, the preparation of those desiring a career in
social science and law and the training of those primarily
interested in business, Smith's courses in the broad field of
economic geography served both purposes. The courses
in industrial management and related areas, however,
were geared more specifically to those interested in the
business world.

Just as Smith entered the field of geography in a rather
chance manner, so also did he become interested in industrial management. A course in this field was first
offered in 1904, in the newly established Evening School
of Accounts and Finance. Smith was not scheduled to
teach industrial management, but he took it over at the
request of Johnson and Dr. Meade, the director of the
Evening School, when the regular instructor could not

[38]*Catalogue of the University of Pennsylvania,* 1906–07, p. 221.
[39]*Ibid.,* 1907–08, p. 251.

keep his commitment. It was just an extra course to supplement his small income as a beginning instructor.[40] He had no special training in the field and, therefore, his experience was gained largely through experimentation and study. However, as the division of "Geography and Industry" grew in the training of both geography and business students, "Industrial Management" [41] became an important course in both day and evening schools.

Other courses allied with "Industrial Management" which Smith developed and later brought into the undergraduate and graduate divisions were "Business Geography and Industry" and "Industrial Costs and Standards." [42] Smith presented all these specialized courses in relation to a broad economic-geographic framework. In addition, through field work he acquainted the students with the various business aspects of the technological phenomena of production.[43]

The practical course in business and industrial management were popular because they helped answer the need of the time. Just as the period from 1865 to 1900 had been characterized by the autocratic management of the "blood and iron" captains of industry, 1900 through the 1940's was marked by the growth of scientific management. The old empire builders were dying off and their places were being taken by specialists such as investment bankers, corporation attorneys, engineers, and personnel managers. These technically trained men wished to apply rational, inductive methods to business operations. Efficiency was their watchword.

[40]Interview with Dr. Alfred H. Williams, Chairman of the Board of Trustees of the University of Pennsylvania, and a former student of Professor Smith, September 19, 1958.

[41]*Catalogue of the University of Pennsylvania*, 1905–06, p. 224.

[42]*Ibid.*, 1914–15, p. 242.

[43]Interview with Dr. Alfred H. Williams, September 19, 1958.

82

J. RUSSELL SMITH

Smith sought a combination of pertinent economic-geographic factors and sound business policy in his business geography courses. His awareness that the courses should be of practical service in fulfilling the needs of the time was illustrated by the catalogue description of "Industrial Management" for 1914–1915 which stated that the course was "A study of manufacturing organization, individual, partnership, and corporate enterprise. The efficiency movement, as applied to manufacturing." [44]

As in other new fields in which Smith was working, there was a paucity of reference material. This lack again prompted him to write his own books, notably, *The Story of Iron and Steel*[45] and *The Elements of Industrial Management*.[46] Of the two, the latter was more significant. In this book Smith discussed such important questions as the management of modern industrial corporations and the need for technical training, types of business organization, the model factory, wages and prices, and the relations between capital and labor. Attempts were made throughout to show the pertinent interconnection between geographic factors and sound industrial development.

The book was far from being original or a work of art, and in many places Smith's lack of specialized training in the field was made apparent by errors of fact or interpretation.[47] What was important, however, was that he presented contemporary progressive thinking in business management which combined a practical and a humani-

---

[44]*Catalogue of the University of Pennsylvania*, 1914–15, p. 242.

[45]J. Russell Smith, *The Story of Iron and Steel* (New York: D. Appleton & Co., 1908).

[46]J. Russell Smith, *The Elements of Industrial Management* (Philadelphia: J. B. Lippincott Company, 1915).

[47]C. Bertrand Thompson, Review of *The Elements of Industrial Management* by J. Russell Smith, *American Economic Review*, VI (June, 1916), 378.

tarian viewpoint. Thus, in his writings and teaching Smith was critical of authoritative, old-school management conducted along military lines; instead, he advocated as good business a high morale among the workers, stemming from clean, safe, attractive plants, fair wages, bargaining power, health and economic benefits, and advancement opportunities.

Significant, also, and still somewhat *avant garde*, were the planned cities he advocated as a means of checking the curse of slums and the turmoil of reconstruction accompanying industrial growth. Again, Smith's "garden city" was not original with him. Ebenezer Howard was leader of the movement, which originated in England, and Smith gave full credit to him as the world's greatest town planner. He considered Howard's attempt to eliminate the crowding evil from the manufacturing town as one of the most important social experiments in Europe.[48] Smith, however, was characteristically alert in grasping the impact of Howard's plan as a means of stemming the evils attendant upon the rapid industrialization of America.[49]

Smith's enthusiasm for the planned city, scientific management, and the industrial potential of America was also voiced in a special issue of the *Annals of the American Academy of Political and Social Science* entitled "The American Industrial Opportunity." Smith, together with other distinguished leaders in such fields as economics, geography, political science, government, and industrial relations, attempted to analyze the factors that caused the recurrent pattern of financial stress in a land rich in resources and potential. The soundness of Smith's philosophy can be evaluated from his following statement:

[48] Smith, *The Elements of Industrial Management*, pp. 114–23.
[49] J. Russell Smith, "The Reconstructed City," *Annals of the American Academy of Political and Social Science*, LIX (May, 1915), 283–89.

The American industrial opportunity is the greatest that the world has ever offered to a numerous people. It is in brief to stop wasting resources, material and human, to apply scientific management to our productive efforts and to increase the potentiality of our effort by better education and through continued promotion of scientific research. Above all, we must master the paralysis of industrial depression and banish unemployment from a hungry world. This will give the materials for a long and much needed increase in wages.[50]

That Smith was chosen to be the editor of this important issue of the *Annals of the American Academy of Political and Social Science* was an indication of the esteem in which he was held for his work in economic geography and scientific business management.

In tracing the physical growth of the department of Geography and Industry, it is interesting to compare Smith's first year with his final one at Wharton. Beginning with three undergraduate day courses in geography in 1903, either Smith or his assistants, in 1919, were teaching thirteen highly diversified courses in the undergraduate day session, some with several sections, ten courses in the graduate division, and ten in the evening school. Thus, under Smith's leadership, geography and allied fields caught fire at Wharton and became an integral part of the curriculum.

STUDENTS AND PERSONNEL TRAINED BY SMITH

Another of Smith's contributions at Wharton was the high calibre of personnel and students he attracted and trained. He recognized the value of a good faculty and

[50]J. Russell Smith, "Foreword" on "The American Industrial Opportunity," *Annals of the American Academy of Political and Social Science*, LIX (May, 1915), xii.

encouraged promising students to go further in the field. Some of his students later became members of the Department of Geography and Industry at Wharton; others went on to distinguished careers in other universities, in government service, and in industry.

In addition to Tower, Smith had a long line of able assistants. George B. Roorbach, another gifted teacher and researcher, assisted Smith from 1911 to 1919 in both physical and economic geography. He was interested in geographic theory and methods as seen in his 1914 report "on the present and possible future development of geography," compiled with Smith's encouragement.[51] After Roorbach left Wharton he joined the then new Harvard School of Business as a professor of geography and foreign trade.

In 1909 Smith brought Alfred White to Wharton from the United States Bureau of Mines to teach sections of "Resources and Industries of the United States." White was chosen because of his broad knowledge of natural resources and the mining industry as well as for his systematic and scholarly approach. His thoroughness in research was valued by Smith because of the latter's tendency at times to skip over facts in his pursuit of an idea. Smith said that he needed a detail man like White on his coattail to challenge his conclusions.[52] After Smith left Wharton, White went back into government service.

Two brothers, Malcolm and John Keir, also saw service under Smith. Malcolm Keir came to Wharton in 1910 from Wesleyan. He left in 1919 to become a professor of economics at Dartmouth. John Keir taught at Wharton from 1913 to 1915 and then went to the Carnegie Institute of Technology. The outstanding work he did as a consultant

[51]*Supra*, Chap. II, pp. 28–29.
[52]Interview with Dr. Joseph H. Willits, May 18, 1959.

to the Dennison Manufacturing Company led to his being chosen their chief economic advisor, then president of the company, and finally chairman of the board.

In a letter to Smith, John Keir reflected a feeling common to other staff members when he said:

I have never forgotten how you rubbed into us very junior members of your staff at Penn that any new idea should be examined, however odd it might appear. And that famous and rugged seminar of yours gave us a set of tools to help in assaying such ideas. As the years have gone over my head, both of these things have served me well—a debt to you which I am glad to have the chance to acknowledge gratefully.[53]

An example of one of Smith's outstanding students was Dr. Joseph H. Willits. He found Smith's summer course at Swathmore, in 1911, so inspiring that he decided to take graduate work under him at Wharton.[54] Willits' first position in the department was as a quizmaster. Later he became a full-time member and was designated by Smith to succeed him as chairman of the department. In 1933, Willits became Dean of the Wharton School. After retirement in 1939, and until 1954, he was Director of Social Science for the Rockefeller Foundation. At present he is in charge of the Educational Survey of the University of Pennsylvania.

Still another outstanding student, who foresook law for geography because of Smith's inspiration, was Dr. Lester Earl Klimm.[55] For many years he has been a professor of geography at Wharton. With Otis Starkey, one

[53]Letter to Professor Smith from John Keir, August 12, 1952.
[54]Interview with Dr. Joseph H. Willits, May 18, 1959.
[55]Interview with Dr. Lester E. Klimm, July 17, 1957.

of Smith's former students at Columbia, he wrote the text *Introductory Economic Geography*.[56]

Dr. Alfred H. Williams who similarly was diverted from the study of law has also had a distinguished career. He was a graduate student of Smith's and subsequently became his assistant. In 1924, he was made Professor of Industry and, in 1939, Dean of the Wharton School. He left the University of Pennsylvania in 1941 to become President of the Federal Reserve Bank of Philadelphia and remained in that position until 1958. At present, although retired from business, he is still active as Chairman of the Board of Trustees of the University of Pennsylvania.

The above men were representative of some of Smith's students. Many others of similar high calibre could be mentioned, indicating that Smith was a good judge of men. All attested unreservedly to the genius of Smith, his keen interest in the younger men in the profession, and the enthusiasm he inspired in them.

SMITH'S TEACHING METHOD

Smith's teaching methods were basic to the thorough training he gave students, especially on the graduate level. Usually Smith did not show to best advantage in a large freshman course. His manner was dry, incisive, and introverted, and his delivery poor because of a slight lisp and a low, monotonous way of speaking.[57] However, in the major seminars, such as "Geographic Seminar," [58] and the smaller lecture-discussion advanced classes, Smith's ability was apparent. The more serious, mature students put him

[56]Lester E. Klimm, Otis P, Starkey, and Norman F. Hall, *Introductory Economic Geography* (New York: Harcourt, Brace and Co., 1937).

[57]Interview with Dr. Alfred H. Williams, September 19, 1958.

[58]*Catalogue of the University of Pennsylvania*, 1907–08, p. 326.

at ease and in the intimacy of the small group he was thought to be inspiring and fascinating.

Dr. Klimm echoed a familiar comment about Smith when he said, "He had ideas every five minutes." [59] Other former students admitted that Smith was not a particularly good lecturer, but agreed with Dr. Williams' statement that "he captivated you by his mind, his spirit, and his intellectual excitement." [60] Smith's enthusiasm for his subject and his ability to make it applicable to everyday reality gave geography new life and meaning and won him inspired followers at Wharton.

Smith considered method basic to developing thinking and creativity and gradually perfected procedures to attain his objectives. Most important was his method of teaching research. He started his famous research seminars at Wharton and further perfected them at Columbia. His aim was to develop "the three qualities of curiosity, ability to recognize similarities, and to evaluate the relative value of data." [61] Although he required exhaustive research, he believed that facts were meaningless until they were organized into ideas. Thus, Smith maintained that the seminar paper, or any research paper, should be highly analytical and aim toward major concepts basic to the nature of geography.

A typical seminar of Smith's at Wharton and later at Columbia proceeded along the following lines: At the beginning of the seminar course each student was in-

[59]Interview with Dr. Lester E. Klimm, July 17, 1957.

[60]Interview with Dr. Alfred H. Williams, September 19, 1958.

[61]J. Russell Smith, "The Seminar, Research, and Geographical Writing." This is an unpublished paper on the conduct of geographical seminars, delivered at a joint meeting of the Association of American Geographers and the American Society of Professional Geographers held in Madison, Wisconsin, on December 28, 1948. Although delivered at a later date than the period under discussion, this paper is pertinent because it deals with Smith's research methodology.

structed to choose a subject for a forty-minute paper. The seminar ran for three hours and the student assigned to a session furnished each of the members with an outline of his paper and a list of sources of information. The seminar paper was read by the author, and at the end of its presentation Smith called upon each member for his criticism. Some of the leading items covered were: main ideas, human interest developed, amount of importance given each subitem, organization of materials, balance of items, and the total critical evaluation of the paper by the students. The finale was the detailed analysis of the paper by Smith and other professors in attendance.[62]

From his experience, Smith learned that in practically every seminar some students read what they considered to be a paper which, in reality, was just undigested material. After discussion had pulled the paper to pieces, the student would more likely emerge with two or more clear-cut ideas. The seminar had forced him to think out conclusions from the facts. It gave him a plan of organization and he was then ready to begin writing. Smith felt that this was a thrilling moment for the student and valuable for all participants.[63]

Another technique was his emphasis on practical field experience. He considered it necessary for his students to get into the actual environment so as to have insight into the economic-geographic process. After they had participated in the real situation, with all its complexities, he expected them to draw their own conclusions. Accordingly, he sponsored field trips to various industrial plants, arranged for work experience in business, and invited guest lecturers who were experts in their fields. Sometimes he assigned students to just look at a piece of

[62]Interview with Dr. Alfred H. Williams, September 19, 1958.
[63]Smith, "The Seminar, Research, and Geographical Writing," p. 7.

property and consider what economic potentialities it might have. At all times, his faculty and students were supposed to "live" the subject. On their vacations and in other free time, he encouraged them to travel, question, and visit. Alfred White often talked about the trip which he took through the Shenandoah Valley when he ran out of money and had to walk part of the way home.[64] In the summer of 1914, Willits made a survey of all the agricultural experiment stations from Philadelphia to Georgia. In 1912–1913, Smith himself made an extended tour of southern Europe and North Africa to study the nature of dry subtropical agriculture and the possible utilization of tree crops. At other times he took trips through the United States, Europe, and the Far East. Later, many of Smith's students applied his methods to their own teaching.

In summarizing Smith's main gifts as a teacher, as early exhibited at the Wharton School, his old colleague Walter Sheldon Tower probably put it best when he said:

In my opinion Dr. Smith has made three lasting impressions in the field of geography. First, I would put his ability and practice in making students and colleagues think. Sometimes, perhaps often, the thinking was stimulated from an impulse to disagree, but whatever the motive force, the thinking was inevitable.[65]

SMITH'S YEARS AT WHARTON IN RETROSPECT

Thus, Smith's years at Pennsylvania were fruitful, not only for his own growth, but also for that of the Wharton

[64]Interview with Dr. Joseph H. Willits, May 18, 1959.
[65]Letter to the writer from Walter Sheldon Tower, in answer to queries about Professor Smith, November 13, 1955.

School and the field of geography. It was here that he developed the first true courses in human-economic geography. It was here, too, that he formulated many of his major ideas and methods, wrote a large part of his best-known advanced books, and perhaps did his most creative work. The Wharton School still bears evidence of Smith's influence. Among Smith's courses still being offered are: "Seminar in Industry," "Manufacturing Industries of the United States," "Industrial Management," and "Field Work in Industry." There are also economic geography courses covering the major regions of the world. Klimm, Willits, and Williams are still connected with the University of Pennsylvania.

V

Smith's Work at the School
of Business, Columbia University

SMITH CAME TO THE SCHOOL OF BUSINESS IN 1919 AT THE
request of President Nicholas Murray Butler.[1] Butler had
been highly impressed by *Industrial and Commercial
Geography* and Smith's outstanding reputation at Wharton. He wanted Smith to organize economic geography in
the School of Business on a basis similar to that at the
Wharton School.[2] Butler designated him Professor of Economic Geography, in charge of the Department.[3] This
position was created especially for Smith and was the first
of its kind in the world. In the courses and methods he
subsequently developed, Smith brought a large part of the
Wharton School to Columbia.

SMITH'S ROLE IN THE EXPANSION
OF GEOGRAPHY AT COLUMBIA

In 1916, the School of Business of Columbia University

[1]Interview with Professor Smith, July 21, 1953.
[2]*Ibid.*
[3]While teaching at Columbia, Smith commuted to his home in Swarthmore, Pennsylvania. He also kept his farm in Round Hill, Virginia.

was founded in order to give specialized training to those interested in pursuing careers in commerce, industry, and finance. It was designated for several categories of students: graduate students who were candidates for the M.S. degree, students who had completed two years of college study or the equivalent, special or nonmatriculated students, and those who were candidates for certificates in secretarial studies and in business.[4]

Because of the newness of the school the curriculum was still in flux. The work in economic geography was somewhat sketchy, consisting at the most of a course or two in the Extension Division.[5] Thus, to a large extent, Smith had less to start with at Columbia than at Wharton. One of the first things Smith did was to work toward making geography a required subject. Some progress was made in 1920, when the School of Business recommended that "Geography 9-10, Economic Geography" be taken during the first two years of college.[6] Previous to this time only commercial geography had been offered. The following year brought real success, when two semesters of economic geography became a prerequisite for matriculation in the School of Business.[7]

Another point of concern was the necessity for graduate work which was requisite to the growth of human-economic geography. Two very basic problems were involved here. First, there was the traditional prejudice of the liberal arts faculties against the granting of advanced degrees by professional schools. Their contention was that

[4]*Columbia University Bulletin of Information*, 1919–1920, 19th Ser., No. 21 (New York: The Arbor Press, Inc., April 14, 1919), pp. 5–6.

[5]Thurman W. Van Metre, *A History of the Graduate School of Business, Columbia University* (New York: Columbia University Press, 1954), p. 45.

[6]*Columbia University Bulletin of Information*, 1920–1921, 20th Ser., No. 28, p. 8.

[7]*Ibid.*, 1921–1922, 21st Ser., No. 26, p. 15.

such degrees as the Master of Arts and the Doctor of
Philosophy should be limited to strictly academic fields
with concentration on pure research. Since economic
geography was included in the School of Business, its
future was partly tied to that of the professional school.
The other basic problem was the dominance of physiography and geology at Columbia University.

The 1920's however, marked a growing strength and
recognition of professional schools and a more liberal
policy towards the introduction of new areas of study
with both undergraduate and graduate status. The School
of Business and human-economic geography accordingly
benefited from these trends.

Initially, the opening gap was made by the Union
Theologial Seminary, whose faculty started petitioning as
early as 1912 for the right to grant the Doctor of Philosophy degree. Though not achieved at this time, a greater
degree of autonomy was established.[8] Various other professional schools entered the campaign for liberalization
and in 1915, the Master of Science degree was set up for
candidates in the Faculties of Medicine, Applied Science
and Practical Arts, and the School of Architecture and the
Master of Laws degree was established for those in the
Faculty of Law.[9] The Master of Arts degree was restricted
to those registered under the Faculties of Political Science,
Philosophy, and Pure Science for nonprofessional work.
Gradually, however, candidates from professional schools
were admitted to the Master of Arts program and in 1921
it was specifically provided that students from certain

[8]Minutes of the Meeting of the Committees on Instruction of the
Faculties of Political Science, Philosophy, and Pure Science, Columbia
University, February 9, 1912.

[9]Minutes of the Meeting of Joint Committee on Instruction, Faculties
of Political Science, Philosophy, and Pure Science, Columbia University,
December 2, 1915.

Columbia professional schools such as the Schools of
Business, Journalism, Architecture, and Practical Arts,
should be deemed eligible for admission to candidacy for
the Master of Arts, subject to the ruling of the Dean of
Admissions as to the equivalency of the professional
school's B.A. with that of Columbia.

After the professional schools had largely gained the
right to the Master's degree, they proceeded to work for
a similar power with respect to the Doctor of Philosophy.
During the 1920's, the rapidly increasing demand for the
Ph.D. in applied fields not comprised within the traditional Graduate Faculties aided the cause of professional
schools. The Union Theological Seminary again led the
way when, in 1921, permission was given to grant the
degree of Doctor of Theology. Two years later the Faculty
of Law was allowed to prepare students for both the
Ph.D. and the Doctor of Laws. Finally, in 1924, students
primarily enrolled in the School of Business could matriculate for the degree of Doctor of Philosophy under the
general regulations of the Faculties of Political Science,
Philosophy, and Pure Science, subject to the approval
of the Joint Committee on Instruction of the Graduate
Faculties and the recommendation of the Director of the
School of Business.[10]

The gradually improving status of the professional
schools and the recognition of their right and ability to
conduct graduate work helped open the way for the
establishment of geography as a separate field of study.
Under the new arrangements, students working in geography at the School of Business could matriculate for a
Master's or Doctor's degree. However, they could not

[10]*Columbia University Bulletin of Information*, 1924–1925, Vol. II,
24th Ser., No. 37, 13–14.

major in geography but only in the fields included under the Graduate Faculties such as history, economics, geology, or physiography. Because of this dilemma, Smith and others of the Department of Economic Geography fought for the establishment of advanced work and degrees in geography. Realization came in 1926 with the establishment of the Committee on Advanced Instruction and Degrees in Geography, to work under the supervision of the Joint Committee on Instruction of the Graduate Faculties. This new committee was to function with respect to advanced degrees in geography in the same manner as a department.[11]

The Report of the Committee on Advanced Instruction and Degrees in Geography, originally appointed in 1925 to study the status of geography and chaired by Dean Pegran, clearly showed the recognition given to economic geography. Here, for the first time, it was clearly stated by members of the Graduate Facilities that

. . . such combinations of Physiography and other subjects as constitute geographies are all of equal importance. In fact, one of them, Economic Geography, which is economics as influenced by physiographic factors, is of outstanding importance. . . . It appears that the term Geography has come to refer quite commonly to Economic Geography.[12]

Recognition was also given to the increasing need of graduate students to be permitted and encouraged to study at Columbia for advanced degrees in geographical fields

[11]*Ibid.*, 1926–1927, Vol II, 26th Ser., No. 43, 7–8; "Report of Committee on Advanced Instruction and Degrees in Geography," March 1, 1926, *Minutes of the Joint Committee on Graduate Instruction*, Columbia University, Vol. II ,124–34.

[12]"Report of Committee on Advanced Instruction and Degrees in Geography," March 1, 1926, p. 129.

and to become candidates for both the Master of Arts and Doctor of Philosophy degrees.

The Committee also presented a program of study for the doctoral candidate, based on that worked out by Professor Douglas Johnson of the Faculty of Pure Science and Professors Smith and John E. Orchard of the School of Business. The program included fifteen to twenty points in Physiography, fifteen to twenty points in Economic Geography, and twenty to thirty credits of more detailed work chosen from Economic Geography, Physiography, Economics, History, Government, Botany, Zoology, Anthropology, or other fields.[18] Thus, the new program gave a wide scope of preparation necessary for advanced training in geography, which previously had been impossible to obtain at Columbia.

The establishment of human-economic geography as a fully recognized subject with graduate status was both a personal triumph for Smith and a milestone in the development of the field at Columbia, where physiography had formerly reigned unchallenged. Also, because of Columbia's prestige in academic circles, the new recognition accorded to human-economic geography undoubtedly influenced a more favorable attitude in other schools.

Then, too, the establishment of geography as a new field of graduate study and the creation of appropriate administrative machinery set a precedent at Columbia for the development of new fields, especially those growing out of the increasingly important professional schools. By 1930, a liberalized program had been set up to accommodate graduate students who desired degrees in fields not covered by the Graduate Faculties. In 1932, special Standing Committees similar to that originally established

[18]*Ibid.*, pp. 130–31.

for Geography were formed to supervise the work for the Doctor of Philosophy degree in Industrial Engineering, Pharmacology, and Nutrition.[14] After this, the development of new specializations was considered a matter of course.

Smith's active role in winning recognition for economic geography at Columbia can thus be counted as among his important contributions to the growth of geography as a professional discipline at Columbia. At the same time, his work was also significant in the movement to gain recognition for the professional school and to encourage the establishment of new fields of undergraduate and graduate study.

From 1926 on, the work in economic geography continued to expand and a broad background in regional-economic geography became a requirement for advanced geographic research.[15] Smith, assisted by Professors John Orchard and Herman Otte, offered a broad study of regional-economic geography and a program of advanced training in geographic scholarship. In 1944, the year of Smith's retirement, geography was a respected and integral part of the School of Business.

SMITH'S DEVELOPMENT OF ECONOMIC GEOGRAPHY AT COLUMBIA

At Columbia Smith continued his work in developing regional, human-economic geography in place of the old industrial-commercial study of the world. Eventually courses were established that dealt with the economic-

[14]Minutes of the Meeting of the Joint Committee on Graduate Instruction, Columbia University, December 1, 1932.

[15]*Columbia University Bulletin of Information*, 1926–1927, Vol. II, 26th Ser., No. 43, 11–12.

geographic analysis of all the continents. Of the seven courses that Smith taught in his beginning year at Columbia, four had a regional-economic orientation.[16] The areas dealt with were Europe, Asia, Africa, and Australia.[17] Although the organizing framework was political, each area was divided into natural regions based on surface, drainage, soil, minerals, climate, and vegetation. Then, analysis was made of the economic use man made of a particular natural region. Smith believed that a human-use approach led to a better understanding of the economic life, special problems, and foreign relations of countries.

In 1920, two more regional courses were added, "Commercial Geography of China" and "Economic Geography of North America." [18] The latter was of particular significance because from it developed Smith's book *North America*.[19] Though, in part, derived from "Economic and Commercial Geography of the United States" and "Resources of the United States" developed at Wharton, "The Economic Geography of North America," like the other courses at Columbia, went much further in applying the human-use regional principle.

In reference to the course "Economic Geography of Africa and Australia," [20] emphasis was again placed on studying these areas both as separate entities and as part of a dynamic, interdependent world. The great unused

[16]*Columbia University Bulletin of Information,* 1919–1920, 19th Ser., No. 21, 26–27.

[17]These regional courses were, "Business 87—Economic Geography of Europe," "Business 88—Economic Geography of Asia," "Business 91—Economic Geography of Africa and Australia," and "Business 92—Economic Geography of Latin America."

[18]*Columbia University Bulletin of Information,* 1920–1921, 20th Ser., No., 28, 32–33.

[19]J. Russell Smith, *North America* (New York: Harcourt, Brace and Company, 1925).

[20]*Columbia University Bulletin of Information,* 1919–1920, 19th Ser., No. 21, 27.

potential of these continents upon their development were given close attention.

Smith's treatment of the regional-economic geography of Europe and Latin America was also important. Europe was a natural focus for most geographers because of its long historical significance, but a detailed course on Latin America was rare at the time. In analyzing the countries of Latin America, Smith again used the human-use natural region set in a broad political framework.

With the establishment of these courses in the early 1920's the basic pattern was laid for the pioneering development of regional-economic geography at Columbia. In general, Smith's regional method did not advance much beyond the human ecological approach characteristic of the 1920's, for he lacked the technical training requisite for modern regional analysis. However, his course work was important in pointing up the necessity of using a regional orientation and a human focus in economic geography. Some might consider his emphasis on human geography as a narrowing of perspective. However, the applied nature of the department within a school of business was in harmony with making man and his economic activities the central theme. It must be remembered, too, that physical geography was not ignored, since the natural environment figured in every course and geomorphology was required for the advanced seminars.

Some may also question Smith's ability to specialize in all areas of the world. He had a relatively good knowledge of North America and Latin America, and he received aid from Professor John Orchard and others on the Far East and Africa. However, Smith was far from being an expert in all world areas. Again, his chief contribution was in his organization of regional-economic geography courses covering most parts of the world rather than in intensive scholarship resulting in the addition of new and original material to the field.

Provisions for a Wider Student Body

Smith wrote his books for a wide audience, not just the specialist, in order to open geography to as many people as possible. His advanced regional courses were geared to meet the needs of those interested in such varied careers as area specialist, resource analyst, regional planner, member of the consular service, expert in foreign trade and investment, and specialist in economic geography. Provision was also made for students with little or no background in geography through the development in 1923–24 of "Geography 1-2,—Economic Geography." It was an "Introductory but non-technical course designed as part of a liberal education." [21]

Smith's Contributions to Methodology

At Columbia Smith refined the methods he had developed at Wharton. Again his skill in teaching research was in evidence, especially in his well-known seminar "Geographic Research," introduced in 1924. His emphasis on ideas as the objective of research was strengthened and was probably his most important contribution to the seminar method at both Wharton and Columbia.[22]

A familiar student evaluation of his seminars was as follows:

[21]*Columbia University Bulletin of Information,* 1923–1924, Vol. II, 23rd Ser., No. 43, 43.

[22]Letter to the author from Dr. Otis P. Starkey, Professor of Geography, Indiana University, August 7, 1956.

In Smith's seminars his students realized they were under the direction of a man who is master of his field. He criticized ruthlessly the errors of his students. They accepted the criticism because they knew Smith was right. . . . I wish I had had about four or six of those seminars—the most worthwhile teaching I ever experienced.[23]

Smith was quick to pick up any slip and was always eager for new information He criticized frankly, but he never objected to criticism of himself if he felt it was worthwhile. At the same time, he was never severe or unkind to the occasional sub-standard student who could not do better than a C.[24]

Frequently, too, Smith used very interesting devices for motivating discussion.

On one occasion he started the seminar by having one of the students read a rough draft for a paper. The paper had so many deficiencies that he and almost everyone else jumped on it. At the end of the hour he said, "Thank you very much; I wrote that paper; now that you have been honest with me, you won't mind if I criticize your papers." [25]

Occasionally, especially toward the end of the semester, he would bring in a paper which was known to be a chapter of a book he was writing. As he read it, students noted that he frequently produced the same errors he had taught them to avoid. At the close of the paper he asked for criticism to check to see how many students had learned what he had taught.[26]

[23]*Ibid.*
[24]Letter to the writer from Dr. Otis P. Starkey, Professor of Geography, Indiana University, August 7, 1956.
[25]*Ibid.*
[26]Letter to the writer from Dr. Benjamin F. Lemert, Professor of Geography, Duke University, August 9, 1956.

As at Wharton, Smith emphasized field work and direct experience for his students. Geography had to be "lived" by travel and field research and not just learned vicariously by reading and study. He illustrated his belief by citing his research for *North America*. For example, his trips to California aided him in writing the chapter entitled "The Valley and Coast of Southern California." His visit to the West Indies formed the basis of the section called "The West Indies—Trade Wind Isles." [27] In 1925–26 he went to Asia on an extensive geographic field trip. Throughout his teaching career he also conducted agricultural experiments at his farm at Round Hill, Virginia— a good example of the blending of the practical and the theoretical.

Despite the few facilities for an interdisciplinary approach at the time, Smith's philosophy of the all-inclusive nature of geography led him to encourage students to gain a working knowledge of the various natural and social sciences.[28] Thus, in methodology, Smith emphasized creative field work and research, a broad scientific approach, experimentation, and correlation with other subject areas.

Smith's Training of Students and Personnel

At Columbia Smith trained able students and developed a faculty of high calibre. A familiar estimate was Van Metre's observation that:

Another characteristic that distinguished Smith as a teacher was his interest in the younger men in his profession and his

[27] J. Russell Smith, unpublished Memorandum to Members of the Council of the Association of American Geographers, April 17, 1942.

[28] Smith, "The Seminar, Research, and Geographical Writing," pp. 7–10.

singular ability to select promising ones to follow in his footsteps as students and teachers. There are few of the older men in the teaching profession who have had as large a group of loyal and brilliant disciples emerge from their classrooms.[29]

His students followed varied fields, some went into teaching, some into government service, and others pursued business careers. Unfortunately, few students received their doctorates under him because after the mid-thirties he was seldom at Columbia—at the most only two or three days a week. This was due to his writing schedule, his leaves for travel and study, and the fact that he commuted to his home in Swarthmore. The Doctors of Philosophy he did produce, however, distinguished themselves in their respective fields. They were Millard Faught, Walter Kollmorgen, Benjamin Lemert, Russell Lynch, Herman Otte, George T. Renner, Otis P. Starkey, and Louis A. Wolfanger. Of the eight, four were listed later in *Who's Who in America*.[30]

Millard Faught[31] received his degree in 1944 and has worked exclusively in business and government service. In 1946, he organized his own company, Faught Company, Inc., which does consultation work on management policy, economics, community problems, and public relations. He also has done writing in his field. He is also founder and director of the Retirement Council, Incorporated.

Walter Kollmorgen[32] accredited himself in teaching and

[29]Van Metre, *A History of the Graduate School of Business, Columbia University*, p. 45.

[30]The four are Faught, Kollmorgen, Renner, and Starkey.

[31]"Millard Faught," *Who's Who in America*, 1960–61 (Chicago: Marquis—Who's Who Inc., 1957), pp. 917–18.

[32]"Walter Kollmorgen," *Who's Who in America*, 1960–61, p. 1623.

in government service as an agricultural economist after receiving his degree in 1940. In 1946 he became Associate Professor of Geography at the University of Kansas, and in the following year, full professor and head of the Department.

Benjamin Lemert received his degree in 1933. He is now Professor of Geography in the Department of Economics and Business Administration of Duke University.

Russell Lynch, who received his degree in 1942, is Chairman of the Department of Geography of Oklahoma Agricultural and Mechanical College.

Herman Otte, who began teaching under Smith at Columbia in 1934, received his degree in 1940. He is now Professor of Economic Geography in the Graduate School of Business.

The late George T. Renner, Jr.[33] resembled Smith in many ways because of his similar breadth of interest, long teaching experience, government service, and numerous writings. He received his doctorate in 1927 and taught in several outstanding universities before coming to Columbia in 1936. He served as Professor of Geography in Teachers College until his death in 1955. His writing ability was demonstrated in his many texts and in his numerous contributions to popular and professional magazines and journals. Renner had great respect for Smith as a geographer and teacher and caught his enthusiasm for conservation, land use, and the whole framework of human-economic geography.

Otis P. Starkey[34] received three degrees from Columbia, the doctorate being granted in 1939. Originally he had planned to go into banking, but his association with Smith

[33]"George T. Renner, Jr.," *Who's Who in America*, 1956–57, p. 2133.
[34]"Otis P. Starkey," *Who's Who in America*, 1960–61, p. 2752.

turned him to geography. He was Assistant Professor of Geography at the University of Pennsylvania from 1931–42 and also lectured at Columbia during 1945–46 and the summer of 1948. He also did editorial work on Smith's texts from 1928 to 1932. From 1946 to 1956 he was Professor of Geography at Indiana University and chairman of the department. His outstanding service with the War Department, 1942–45, won for him the Merit Civil Service Award. He is the author with Lester Klimm of *Introductory Economic Geography* (1937) and *Exploring Our Industrial World*[35] (1938), with W. F. Christians. Both books reflected Smith's influence.

Louis Wolfanger served at Columbia for many years as an assistant to Smith and Professor John Orchard, starting in 1923 and continuing until 1939. He is not only an economic geographer but also a soil specialist who has seen service with the Bureau of Chemistry and Soils, United States Department of Agriculture. At present, he is Research Professor in Land Use of the Department of Resource Development of Michigan State University.

The dissertations and specialties of Smith's students were particularly interesting because they showed such diverse aspects of geography.[36] They pointed up Smith's own wide interests as well as the broad approach he gave to geography at Columbia.

In discussing Smith's training of personnel, one can look to the students who have been named, since most of

[35]Otis P. Starkey and William F. Christians, *Exploring Our Industrial World* (Philadelphia: The John C. Winston Co., 1938).

[36]Representative dissertations are Benjamin Lemert's "The Cotton Textile Industry of the Southern Appalachian Piedmont," in industrial geography; Herman Otte's "Industrial Opportunity in the Tennessee Valley of Northwest Alabama," in resource use and regional planning; George T. Renner's "Primitive Religion in the Tropical Forests," in cultural geography.

them rendered service at Columbia before going to other universities or other fields.[37] The only one not mentioned is John Orchard,[38] who was Smith's first assistant and a valuable aide through the years. Orchard received his A.B. from Swarthmore in 1916 and then studied at the University of Pennsylvania during 1917–18. In 1920, Smith brought Orchard from the United States Bureau of Mines where he had been working as a mine economist. In 1923 he received his doctorate from Harvard and became a full-time member of the staff at Columbia. Orchard aided Smith with the development of the regional courses. Since he is an expert on Japan he was especially helpful with the courses on the Far East. His administrative ability has also been important to the department. Smith had little interest in routine details and was chairman in name only when it came to administration. After the mid-thirties when Smith was on campus infrequently, Orchard largely took over the running of the department. Since Smith's retirement in 1944, Professor Orchard has been the Chairman. Orchard also rendered extensive government service, especially during World War II. France awarded him the Legion d'Honneur in 1951 for his work with the Economic Cooperation Administration.

SMITH'S WORK IN PROFESSIONAL GEOGRAPHIC ORGANIZATIONS

When studying the work of one who was a geography teacher, scholar, and author, it is natural to look for his activities in the National Council for Geographic Education and the Association of American Geographers. Surprisingly, Smith never participated actively in the former

[37]All served at Columbia except Millard Faught.
[38]"John Orchard," *Who's Who in America*, 1960–61, p. 2194.

organization.[39] He did attend some of the meetings and contributed to the *Journal of Geography*.

Smith was active, however, in the Association of American Geographers from the earliest days and served as president during 1941–42. He was also among those who wished to liberalize the membership rules so as to admit the younger men in the profession.[40] The change came in 1948 when the American Society for Professional Geographers merged with the Association of American Geographers.

Smith was similarly interested in improving the meetings of the Association of American Geographers by encouraging better scholarship. For example, he was so disturbed by what he considered to be the poor quality of the 1946 meeting, that he made inquiries among other members and circulated a list of needed improvements.[41] He believed that the program should be planned so as to permit time for discussion and the presentation of controversial material. He believed, too, that there should be a greater number of papers on methodology and philosophy. These papers, according to Smith, should be discussed as a total piece of work and make facts subservient to ideas. A screening committee should also be set up to help insure the delivery of scholarly papers.

The inferior quality of the meetings as Smith conceived

[39]Letter to the writer from Dr. George J. Miller, Professor of Geography, Indiana University, in refernce to Professor Smith's work in the National Council of Geography Teachers, now the National Council for Geographic Education, June 28, 1959.

[40]See letters to Professor Smith from the following: Carl O. Sauer, September 12, 1942; Nels Bengston, September 5, 1942; George B. Cressey, September 18, 1942, Photostats are in the possession of the writer. See also Smith's unpublished "Memorandum to Members of the Council of the Association of American Geographers, April 17, 1942."

[41]J. Russell Smith, unpublished memorandum entitled, "Notes on Papers, Discussion, and Procedure at the Meeting of the Association of American Geographers at Columbus, Ohio, December, 1946."

them, led him to believe that there was much poor graduate work. He contended that many members of the association had never been in a first-class seminar, where they had a paper "picked to pieces" either by their instructor or their fellow classmates. He proposed, therefore, that one session of the Association of American Geographers be devoted to the methodology of a geographic seminar. The topic was considered at the 1948 meeting and valuable suggestions were made.[42]

Smith took the Association of American Geographers very seriously because of its role as the most important organization of professional geographers. Accordingly, he felt that all members should make it a channel for their best work. He wrote:

When the call goes out for papers, it should stress the importance to a man's career of papers read in such meetings. Certain it is that of those who are looking for staff members, all are going to draw an opinion of a man from the paper he reads and that opinion will stick a long time. I know personally that men have had calls to first-class universities from the reading of one paper and I have marked good-looking, loud-talking men down for life for three sentences—three thoughtless sentences in a paper read before the Association.[43]

Smith was also a member of the American Geographical Society though not so actively as in the Association of American Geographers.[44]

[42]J. Russell Smith, "The Seminar, Research, and Geographical Writing." This paper was Smith's chief contribution at the 1948 meeting. A whole session was devoted to an investigation of the method of the geographic seminar.

[43]Letter from Professor Smith to George F. Carter, Program Chairman of the 1948 meeting of the Association of American Geographers, April 5, 1948.

[44]In 1956, Smith received the Cullum Geographical Medal from this society.

A FINAL ESTIMATE

Smith's work in course development at Columbia, as well as the Wharton School, exhibited, as did his writings, his growing maturity, creativity, and broadening scope of interest. A process of growth can be seen from his initial work in largely commercial areas to that in regional, human-economic geography. By presenting man in relation to his environment, Smith contributed to making geography at Columbia and the University of Pennsylvania, a social science with implications for all aspects of man's activities. His work placed him among those pioneering educators who helped give geography status and prestige at the college and graduate levels.

His methodology and his ability to produce students and personnel of high calibre also demonstrated his gifts. Although his specific course work was not as influential in spreading his ideas as were his books, the two were so intimately interlinked that one was indispensable to the other. His work in professional organizations again illustrated the high standards and serious goals he set for American geographers. Thus, Smith's contributions to geography as an academic and professional discipline help to explain Smith, the man, the author, and the geographer, and to show his specific role in aiding geography's development as an advanced field of study.

VI

The Contributions of J. Russell Smith
to School Geography

AFTER 1920, SMITH DEVOTED MOST OF HIS EFFORTS TO ELEmentary textbooks. He was motivated to write for this level for two main reasons. In the first place, Smith believed that his work would do the most good if it could influence the minds of children. He said that "most adult activities are bent toward the realization of desires conceived before the age of fifteen years."[1] In the second place, the field of elementary textbook writing was lucrative because of the wider teaching of geography at this level and the demand for a more human approach, which was Smith's forte.

Smith's elementary texts contributed significantly to geographic education. In order to properly evaluate his role in the development of the field, it should be helpful to review briefly the work of those who preceded him, as well as that of his contemporaries.

[1] J. Russell Smith, "How Geography Contributes to General Ends in Education," *The Teaching of Geography*, Thirty-Second Yearbook of the National Society for the Study of Education (Bloomington, Illinois: Public School Publishing Co., 1933), p. 39.

TEXTBOOKS IN ELEMENTARY GEOGRAPHY DURING
THE NINETEENTH CENTURY

Geography textbook writing has followed the lines of development in geographic content and general educational methodology current at the time. Accordingly, the early books, like texts in other fields, were encyclopedic, unscientific, and lacking in organization. They were meant to be memorized and were frequently written in a completely catechetical manner. There were few or no maps and illustrations, or suggested activities for pupils.[2] Thus, the books were chiefly descriptive; casual relations, one of the keynotes of modern geography, were never suggested.[3] Stereotype and curiosities emphasizing the "strange" and "unusual" habits of people and bizarre natural phenomena, together with statistics about people, places, and products, were the points stressed. There was also a strongly religious tone and a more or less static view of the world.

Furthermore, ignorance of child nature was apparent. Little attempt was made to adapt materials to the interests, experience, and vocabulary of children of different age levels. Though the language was at times fairly simple, the ideas often involved general concepts of the earth which adults acquired only by years of experience and study.[4] The method of assign-study-recite procedures worked well with this early approach to elementary geography.

[2]Ella Huntling, "Modern Trends in the Teaching of Geography," *Proceedings of the Fifth Biennial Conference of the World Federation of Education Associations* (Dublin, Ireland: World Federation of Education Associations, 1933), p. 242.

[3]Edgar Dawson, *The Teaching of the Social Studies* (New York: The Macmillan Co., 1928), p. 38. See also Rolla M. Tryon, *The Social Studies as School Subjects* (New York: C. Scribner's Sons, 1935).

[4]Dawson, *The Teaching of the Social Studies,* pp. 40–41.

The books of Jedidah Morse, Congregational clergyman, and Morse's son Sidney were typical of the early books. Jedidiah Morse's *Geography Made Easy* (1784), *The American Geography* (1789), and *Morse School Geography* (1820), the last written with his son, went through numerous editions and were important through the first half of the century.[5]

The First Pedagogical Geographies

Within each period, there are innovators who help initiate the trend to a higher level of development. Such was the case with William C. Woodbridge and Emma Willard, who collaborated in writing a number of elementary texts. The first was *Geography for Beginners* or the *Instructor's Assistant* (1826).[6] Both authors were professionals, Woodbridge in geography and Willard in education. Both were influenced by European leaders, such as Pestalozzi and Ritter.[7] Such principles as a conversational style intelligible to children, an attempted grading of subject matter, and memorization after "inquiry" characterized their work.

Woodbridge wrote several texts of his own. Among these was *Rudiments of Geography*, published in 1820.[8] This book also attempted to make geography learning

[5]Ralph H. Brown, "Letter to Rev. Jedidiah Morse, Author of the *American Universal Geography*," *Annals of the Association of American Geographers*, XLI (September, 1951), 187–92.

[6]Albert Perry Brigham and Richard E. Dodge, "Nineteenth Century Textbooks of Geography," *The Teaching of Geography*, Thirty-Second Yearbook of the National Society for the Study of Education (Bloomington, Illinois: Public School Publishing Co., 1933), p. 9.

[7]Lorrin G. Kennamer, Jr., "Beginnings in Geographic Education," *Journal of Geography*, LII (February, 1953), 73–74.

[8]Brigham and Dodge, "Nineteenth Century Textbooks of Geography," 9.

more natural. The technique Woodbridge used was that of journey geography focused around a fictional child. Starting with the classroom, the text led the student into the home community, and then gradually into the whole world. A similar approach was used by others, such as Samuel Worcester in his series of texts which ran from 1819 to 1844, and S. G. Goodrich in his "Peter Parley's" geography stories for children.[9] By 1850, atlases, maps, graphs, and illustrations came into common usage.[10]

A New Emphasis on Physical Geography

Beginning near the middle of the century, physical geography in the United States started to become an organized science through the work of various eminent American geologists.[11] Woodbridge was one of the early textbook writers who helped introduce physical geography to the grades. In his *Modern School Geography* (1844) he spoke of "the new and interesting methods which have given to physical geography something of the clearness and beauty of a science." [12] The book used the work of Louis Agassiz and the New York State geologists who made their classical surveys during the period. Woodbridge was somewhat ahead of his time, but the trend was continued in the 1860's with the work of Arnold Guyot, David Warren, and Matthew Maury.

[9]*Ibid.*, 11.

[10]Orville A. Roorbach, *Biblioteca Americana, 1820–1852* (New York: Peter Smith, 1939). This index to American publications during these thirty years indicated the increased attention to geography, particularly in reference to maps, gazateers, and physical geography. Pertinent listings are found on pp. 34, 59, 70, 98, 103, 105, 117, 144, 147, 179, 213–15,224, 241, 271, 278–79, 301, 371, 415–16, 425, 509, 595.

[11]Note, Appendix, pp. 208–10. See also Roorbach, *Biblioteca Americana, 1820–1852* and Supplements for 1852–55, 1855–58, 1858–61.

[12]Brigham and Dodge, "Ninetheenth Century Textbooks of Geography," p. 12.

Guyot, the most important of the three,[13] was a trained geographer and long a professor at Princeton University. While abroad, Guyot had studied under Karl Ritter and was probably his greatest disciple. He was a personal friend of Alexander von Humboldt and a firm advocate of the Pestalozzian method. In association with Mary H. Smith of the Oswego Normal School, he wrote a series of four geography texts which followed Pestalozzi's principles.[14] Accordingly, the texts reflected the ideas that all learning was gradual and that thorough understanding preceded memorization. In order to encourage thought, the topical method was used with a gradual change from a descriptive basis to a causal one. Guyot also introduced "type" studies, his books being centered around a series of journeys to "type" regions.

Besides a heavy emphasis on physical geography, Guyot's works contained innovations in physical and political maps with relief shown in two colors and by hachures.[15] Largely as a result of Guyot's work, school geography began to change from a mass of locations, statistics, and descriptions to a physical science.

Guyot's texts, however, were stiff and formal and their full impact was not felt until the work of Colonel F. W. Parker, an ardent follower. Colonel Parker was Superintendent of Schools in Quincy, Massachusetts, and later head of the Cook County Normal School in Chicago. In the latter position, especially, he trained several prominent

[13]Guyot may be considered the most important of the three because he was the leader of the new emphasis on physical geography. He also had a more scholarly knowledge of physical geography and child psychology than either Warren or Maury. Unfortunately his style was dry and uninteresting and thus lacked appeal for students.

[14]Charles Dryer, "A Century of Geographic Education in the United States," *Annals of the Association of American Geographers*, XIV (September, 1924), 125.

[15]Brigham and Dodge, "Nineteenth Century Textbooks of Geography," p. 24.

teachers of geography, such as Alexis Frye, and introduced them to the thinking of Guyot and Ritter. From 1860 to 1900, Parker was one of the leading educators in the movement to recognize and improve the schools.[16]

Maury's and Warren's texts, besides emphasizing physical geography were also quite readable and teachable. In addition, Warren's series were the first to definitely follow the concentric or cycle plan that persisted for so many years. This method was adopted by James Monteith and William Swinton in the 1870's and was later used by Smith and most of his contemporaries.

Influence of the Report of the Committee of Ten on Secondary School Studies

The growth of physical geography was aided by the development of physiography, which became a recognized science during the last fifteen years of the century.[17] The geography conference arranged by the Committee of Ten on Secondary School Subjects of the National Education Association made a momentous report in 1894[18] on adjustments needed in the school curriculum because of the new approach. The Committee unanimously stated that physical geography or physiography, rather than political geography, should be taught in the schools and that the methods of the physical sciences should be used. Influenced by this report, elementary texts were written

[16]Kennamer, "Beginnings in Geographic Education," p. 76.

[17]Brigham and Dodge, "Nineteenth Century Textbooks of Geography," p. 25.

[18]"Report of Geography Conference," *Report of the Committee of Ten on Secondary School Studies,* Published for the National Education Association (New York: American Book Company, 1894), 204–37. Among the seven members of the Geography Conference were: William Morris Davis, Israel C. Russell, and T. C. Chamberlain. See also Dryer, "A Century of Geographic Education in the United States," 220.

along physiographic lines. Notable among the new texts were those of Alexis Frye and the "Natural Series" of Jacques Redway and Russell Hinman.[19] The *Journal of Geography* was created in 1902 by William Davis and others to aid teachers in learning the new geography and the methods of teaching it.

This help was not enough, however. The new school curriculum and texts, with their weight on physiography, were too difficult and strong protests soon arose for simplification. Gradually, between 1900 and 1920, the emphasis shifted from the physical to the human side of geography: "The schoolmen of the country backed up by three or four million children, had decreed that in elementary geography at least, the emphasis does not belong on the physical side."[20]

GEOGRAPHY TEXTBOOK WRITING IN THE
TWENTIETH CENTURY

To meet the need of the changing times, old texts were revised and new ones written which attempted to combine the physical and human aspects of geography. Commercial and later regional-economic geography came to the fore. These innovations were first made on the university level and slowly seeped down to the grades.

The First Attempts Towards Human Geography

The Tarr and McMurry series, first printed in 1900, was one of the early efforts to bridge the transition of

[19]Brigham and Dodge, "Nineteenth Century Textbooks of Geography," pp. 25–26.
[20]Ray H. Whitbeck, "Thirty Years of Geography in the United States," *Jouranl of Geography,* XX (April, 1921), 109–10.

human geography to the elementary level. The work of
these two educators followed the psychological principles
of Pestalozzi and Herbart.[21] The five formal steps of the
Herbartian method, which to a large extent comprise today's teaching plan, were used. Home geography was
applied. The authors also included well-formulated
thought questions for review and study and were the first
to introduce collateral reading and to provide for individual work. The careful grading of material and simplicity of style were other factors which helped make their
books popular.

Despite these innovations and the frequent interweav-
ing of human and natural factors, physical geography still
occupied more than two-thirds of each book.[22] For example, although home geography in story form was used,
students were first introduced to all the factors of the
natural environment. Towards the end, man's industry
and commerce were presented. Thus, their approach was
still far from those objects most familiar and meaningful
to children.

Richard Elwood Dodge's *Elementary Geography*
(1904), and Albert Perry Brigham and Charles McFar-
lane's text of 1916 also attempted to bridge the gap, but
they were still too weighted towards the physical. Educators were fully aware that the texts were not adequate in

[21]Frank and Charles McMurry were among the initiators of the
Herbartian movement in the United States. They helped found the
National Herbart Society which is now the National Society for the
Study of Education. The First, Fourth, Fifth, Fourteenth, Sixteenth,
and Seventeenth Yearbooks and Supplements of this society contain
many pertinent articles on geographic education during the period under
discussion. See for example, Charles A. McMurry, "A Course of Study
in Geography for the Grades of the Common School," *Supplement to*
the Fourth Yearbook of the National Herbart Society (Published by
the Society, 1899), 121–73.

[22]Dryer, "A Century of Geographic Education in the United States,"
p. 229.

providing a necessary human approach. For example, in 1915 Dodge stated in his presidential address before the Association of American Geographers that geography was increasing in significance only in business and commercial courses where the emphasis was on its human aspects. He pointed out that "geography is in a slough of despondency as deep as was the case before the revolutionary report of the Committee of Ten." [23] The lag was especially apparent at the high school level where the emphasis was still largely physiographic. Dodge maintained that a revolution was needed in school geography as epochal as the one of the 1890's to prepare the way for the new geography centered around human groups and their problems.[24] Dodge further remarked that:

Geography is a human as much an earth science. Its larger problems are human problems that involve a study not only of the influencing conditions of the physical environment, but of the economic and social conditions. . . . We must have textbooks in human and physical geography organized scientifically and better unified than many of the current books on commercial geography.[25]

The Effects of World War I

World War I gave increased impetus to the growing demand for a more human approach to geography. Almost

[23]Richard Elwood Dodge, "Some Problems in Secondary Education with Special Reference to Secondary Schools," *Annals of the Association of American Geographers,* VI (1916), 14. See also Paul F. Griffin, "The Contribution of Richard Elwood Dodge to Educational Geography" (unpublished Ph.D. dissertation, Faculty of Philosophy, Columbia University, 1952), pp. 109–53, 208–10, 212–16.

[24]Dodge, "Some Problems in Geographic Education with Special Reference to Secondary Schools," p. 18.

[25]*Ibid.,* 15.

every child knew someone who was going overseas. People and their problems rather than just physical geography were stressed and foreign lands came closer to home. Maps were used more meaningfully in tracing the course of the war or in locating a foreign town mentioned in a relative's letter. In the schools, geography was related to such projects and clothing drives for our allies overseas. Children responded so well to this new approach that, after the war, teachers wanted to continue it. Gradually, geography became recognized as predominantly a human or social science[26] and suitable texts were needed to convey the new spirit.

In 1921, Wallace W. Atwood attempted to solve the textbook problem by using natural regions as his organizing principle.[27] Despite the new features he introduced, however, his text was still largely land-centered. Smith was more successful in conveying a truly human spirit in his first texts also published in 1921.[28]

AN OVERVIEW OF SMITH'S MAIN IDEAS
AND METHODS IN SCHOOL GEOGRAPHY

Smith was not original in many of the features he used in his elementary geographies. However, he so combined old elements with new developments in psychology and social science that his initial works came closer to answering the need for human geography at the elementary level than any other texts of the period. In essence, Smith's

[26]Mendel E. Branom and Fred K. Branom, *The Teaching of Geography* (Boston: Ginn & Co., 1921), pp. 51–52.
[27]Dryer, "A Century of Geographic Education in the United States," p. 127.
[28]J. Russell Smith, *Human Geography, Book One, Peoples and Countries; Human Geography, Book Two, Regions and Trade* (Philadelphia: The John C. Winston Co., 1921).

early books showed how to write human geography for the grades and helped set a pattern for many years to come.

It is fortunate that Smith started writing for the elementary level in the 1920's. By that time he had more than twenty years of teaching experience. He was also an established writer who had developed the facility of translating technical matter into popular and human terms, an ability which is especially necessary in writing for children. His background in economic geography, history, and economics was more fully in keeping with the new emphasis, especially after World War I, of treating geography as primarily a social science. Important, too, was the fact that he had as models the work of the many writers of elementary texts, who for the previous two decades had been attempting to bridge the gap between physical and human geography.

Educational Objectives of Smith's Elementary Texts

From the beginning, Smith's educational aims in writing elementary texts were in terms of social values and general education. As he repeatedly stated, "The chief function of geographers is education—the education of people who are not geographers and never will be geographers." [29] The fact that most professional geographers are teachers substantiates his point.

As viewed within the framework of general education, what were the objectives of geography teaching? Were they to teach the facts of physiography, of political location, or of map reading? No, said Smith, although these and similar elements should be present. Rather, the long-run, major objectives of geography were twofold. The

[29] J. Russell Smith, "Are We Free to Coin New Terms?" *Annals of the Association of American Geographers*, XXV (March, 1935), 19.

most important related to attitudes that helped to interpret the facts of man and his environment. The second consisted of a few ideas about countries and places.[30] Essentially, the ideas laid the basis of understanding necessary for building sound attitudes.

In the hierarchy of attitudes, Smith placed that of the "higher" or "world citizenship," our feeling towards other peoples or nations, as the most basic.[31] This concept was a persistent theme in all his texts. The idea of world citizenship and interdependence may be commonly accepted today, but in the period between the two world wars, when the bulk of Americans advocated isolationism and economic nationalism, Smith's sentiments and those of like mind were rare indeed, especially when expressed in texts. For example, a 1925 research study of the National Education Association pointed up the highly nationalistic tone of our American social studies education. The report showed that a large percentage of the space in history texts and supplementary readers was devoted to wars of the United States. These wars were invariably presented as altruistic or waged in self-defense. Little or no attention was given to the themes of peace, international cooperation, or the problems and needs of the people of the United States or of any other nation. While this specific study was of history texts, the same approach prevailed in others areas of the social studies.[32]

[30]J. Russell Smith, "What Shall the Geography Teacher Teach in the Elementary School?" *Jouranl of Geography*, XLVI (March, 1947), 101.

[31]J. Russell Smith, "Geography and the Higher Citizenship" *Progressive Education*, II (June, 1925), 77–80.

[32]"Keeping Pace With the Advancing Curriculum," *Research Bulletin of the National Education Association*, III (September and November, 1925), 150–56. See also: Ernest Horn, "Possible Defects in the Present Content of American History As Taught in the Schools," *Sixteenth Yearbook of the National Society for the Study of Education* (Bloomington, Illinois: Public School Publishing Co., 1920), 156–73; Peter Ode-

After the devastations of World War I, Smith believed that the concepts and attitudes engendered by the American school system, particularly at the elementary level, were basic factors in determining whether the future world would be one of peace or of international anarchy. He stated that, "the elementary school is the place where geography may render its greatest service to modern society," [33] because at this level a child was first introduced to his country and the rest of the world. During the formative and highly impressionable years of childhood the teacher had the greatest opportunity to implant sound attitudes and basic concepts which could grow through the years with careful cultivation and reinforcement.[34] The "higher citizenship" that Smith advocated was thus built on previously developed attitudes and major ideas, such as positive community living, good citizenship, and the interdependence of people.

Approaches Used By Smith in Achieving His Objectives

How could elementary texts help to develop concepts and attitudes about people and countries, leading to world understanding? Smith's answer to this problem, and his main contribution to elementary geography, was making man the focus of study.

Human geography. According to Smith, if geography were to accomplish its primary social objectives, it had to be interpreted in human terms. For this reason, his

---

gard, *The American Public Mind* (New York: Columbia University Press, 1930), p. 98.

[33]Smith, "How Geography Contributes to General Ends in Education," p. 33.

[34]*Ibid.*, pp. 38–39.

books did not start with essays on soils, landforms, trade, or other factors of physical or economic geography, treated as separate entities. All these elements appeared in his texts, but in "natural relationship to the study of man as he makes his living upon the earth which is his home." [35] By emphasizing people and their common needs and problems, children could more readily develop in sympathy and understanding towards others.

Use of the psychological method. Smith's emphasis on the human focus was in keeping with the psychological principles advocated by Pestalozzi, Herbart, and Dewey. Smith was especially influenced by Dewey's works such as *The Child and the Curriculum, The School and Society,* and *Democracy and Education.*[36] Accordingly, facts, ideas, and attitudes were taught so that they could be put to work in solving problems that arose in the child's own experience. This was the applied science method of mental training by "fact using" rather than "fact stuffing."[37]

Smith consistently stressed cause and effect so that the relationship between factors could be seen. A natural explanation was given of the "hows" and "whys" of a human situation. The psychological method harmonized with the memory process and facilitated understanding because it employed motivation and inductive reasoning in solving a purposeful human problem.

Concerning the psychology of teaching ideas in a meaningful way, Smith frequently referred to a lesson taught him by Lincoln Steffens, the famous muckraking

[35]J. Russell Smith, *Manual for Human Geography,* Books I and II (Philadelphia: The John C. Winston Company, 1922), p. 1.

[36]J. Russell Smith, "Elements of Geography and the Geographic Unit," *School and Society,* XVII (March, 1927), 45.

[37]Smith, "Elements of Geography and the Geographic Unit," p. 47.

journalist and editor of the then famous *Everybody's Magazine*. The lesson Steffens taught Smith about writing for the layman was as follows:

You have an idea—it can be reduced to a simple sentence, but if you state your idea in one sentence, your reader won't get it. You must tell your reader facts that will prepare his mind to receive your idea. This may require several pages. You go along page after page, and finally the mind of the reader is opened up. Then you can drop that sentence in and he can never get it out.[38]

Smith suggested a similar method for the teacher. First, sift through the daily or unit work for the big ideas. Then, prepare a background through well-chosen, interesting facts. Finally, let drop the ideas.[39] A necessary concomitant of this procedure was to proceed from the simple to the more complex in presenting facts and ideas.

The unit of presentation—the human-use approach. Against what framework were the human-geographic facts and ideas to be presented? Smith brought into the elementary school the human-use, natural-region approach which initially he had applied in his advanced texts and college courses.[40] This was the first time in elementary education that man's actual use of the natural environment was made the primary key in setting up regional boundaries for studying the world. Also for the first time on this level, Smith made climatology a basic factor in studying a natural region. Previously, texts had stressed physiography.

[38]Smith, "What Shall the Geography Teacher Teach in the Elementary School," p. 102.
[39]*Ibid.*, p. 103.
[40]J. Russell Smith, "The Use of Type Studies in Elementary Geography." Unpublished article, dated October 6, 1928.

Smith believed that the human-use regional method
facilitated understanding and memory because it emphasized cause and effect relationships, meaningful association, and progression from the known to the unknown
around a human focus. Accordingly, once a norm or type
of region was understood by the child, it became a kind
of "yardstick or tool of measurement" which could be
used over and over again to explain similar situations
without boring repetition. Smith's many cross references
in using maps, pictures, and text material, further pointed
up interrelationships between man and nature in a region
and provided for continuous review and comparison.

Smith usually made a detailed human-use regional
analysis of countries in his texts for the fifth grade and
up. For the third and fourth grades, he largely used type
studies of communities or regions chosen because of their
interest and importance in teaching broad geographic
ideas. As Smith wrote his various elementary texts, he
modified his regional organization. For example, in his
first books such as *Human Gegraphy* (Books I and II),
he used natural divisions, characterized by dominant economic activities. Although natural human-use regions
were more geographic, Smith learned partly from teachers'
reports that they were more difficult for young children
than the familiar names of countries and places. Therefore,
in the 1930's he employed a political framework for his
human-use regions. For example, he used the terminology
"Southern States" [41] in place of the earlier, "The Southern
and Central Plains." [42] The political headings, however,
were for convenience only, since within each political di-

[41] J. Russell Smith, *American Lands and Peoples* (Philadelphia: The
John C. Winston Company, 1932), pp. vi–vii.
[42] Smith, *Human Geography, Book Two, Regions and Trade*, pp. vii–
viii.

vision the interrelationship between human and natural factors was the dominant theme.

Smith's style. All of the above theories would have been of little value if the material had not been written in a manner attractive to children. As Smith stated many times, "There is no good reason why science books should not be interesting except the fact that very few writers know how to make them so." [43] Smith always considered it an important part of his job to make his books interesting.

In composing the elementary texts, he applied the advice given him by the editors of the *Country Gentleman* when he began to write for that well-known periodical. "Mr. Smith, perhaps you think it cannot be done, but every principle of agriculture can be told around the story of a man. Find the man who is applying it. Get his story. Tell it, and by that means bring out the principle." [44] Invariably, an interesting story form became the basis of Smith's writing.

The other keynote of his style was simplicity of language which he also gained in part from writing for popular magazines.[45] Smith frequently admonished fellow geographers not to "coin" new terms unless these terms were capable of being understood by the layman.[46] He believed clarity and simplicity to be essential on the elementary level, especially when viewed in terms of general

[43] Smith, *Manual for Human Geography* (Books I and II), p. 2.
[44] J. Russell Smith, *Geography and the Higher Citizenship* (Philadelphia: The John C. Winston Company, 1925), p. 16.
[45] Especially from 1908 to 1920, Smith wrote successfully on a free-lance basis for such popular periodicals as *Country Gentleman, Everybody's Magazine, Atlantic Monthly, Harper's, Century,* and *Saturday Evening Post.*
[46] Smith, "Are We Free to Coin New Terms?" pp. 20–22.

education. Smith's art in developing his material in an interesting and simple manner made his elementary writings extremely popular and placed him among the most skillful writers of grade-school geographies.

Smith's texts were far from being easy invention. They were the product of his own hard work and that of his assistants. Foremost among the latter was his wife Henrietta whom he praised as "a gifted teacher of the young who has aided me in interpreting material in terms of children's language and interest." [47] The two worked closely together on both the style and content of the elementary texts. The story goes that one of the techniques Smith and his wife developed to test the language of the text was the invention of a fictional character called "Clarence." "Clarence" was somewhat on the slow side and they felt that if "he" could understand what they were saying, anyone could.[48] Smith may have told this story somewhat tongue in cheek but it showed his serious desire to communicate to every child. In addition to "Clarence," Smith also enlisted his own children and others in the neighborhood to get their reaction to his geography stories.

Believing that children and teachers who actually used his books were the real test, he also enlisted the aid of school personnel in typical areas throughout the country. Smith followed many of their suggestions both in writing and revising his books. Of course, he received aid from the editorial staff of the John C. Winston Company, but the main work of Smith's books came from his own hands with the help of his assistants.[49]

[47]Smith, *Human Geography, Book Two, Regions and Trade,* p. iii.

[48]Interview with Dr. Lester E. Klimm, Professor of Geography at the Wharton School of Finance and Commerce of the University of Pennsylvania, July 17, 1957.

[49]Professor Smith enlisted the aid of some of his students such as George T. Renner and Otis P. Starkey in doing research. His son Thomas

The products of Smith's carefully organized procedure were texts that appealed to children while at the same time teaching them basic geographic ideas and attitudes. Few could fail to respond to the story of Okuk and Shoo-e-ging-wa the Eskimo children[50] or Hamkin and Suleika the little Arab brother and sister of the Sahara.[51] The same was true of other interesting fictional characters created by Smith to personalize and make meaningful the peoples of other home and world communities.

Smith's use of correlation. Smith was one of the first writers of elementary geography texts to correlate geography with history and other aspects of the social sciences. His broad approach heightened the human story and enabled students to compare man's past use of the environment with that of the present, and to project into the future. It showed the great changes wrought by scientific discoveries which have enabled man to make fuller use of his environment. Smith never ceased to relate geography to good citizenship, community-mindedness, and conservation. Increasingly he developed a social science approach, with geography as the core because of its role as the synthesizing bridge between man and nature.[52]

The use of correlation and integration did not mean that geography or any of the other subjects lost their identities; rather, all were united in common, long-range goals to give heightened understanding to the dynamic relationship between man and his world.[53] Smith's thinking was

also assisted him in this capacity as well as some of his secretaries such as Myra Light and Margaret Hitch.

[50]Smith, *Human Geography, Book One, Peoples and Countries,* p. 192.
[15]*Ibid.,* p. 286.
[52]Smith, *Human Geography, Book Two, Regions and Trade,* pp. iv, v, vi.
[53]Smith, "How Geography Contributes to General Ends in Education," p. 40.

thus in keeping with modern educational philosophy and the aims of the social studies.

Illustrations, captions, and maps. A multiple-sensory approach to help vitalize and give meaning to abstractions was another psychological principle that Smith initially applied more fully than any of his contemporaries. His illustrations were never merely decorative accessories, but always had a serious educational purpose.[54] From his earliest texts he realized the value of interesting, colorful pictures and maps in developing concrete imagery upon which children could base definite relationship understandings. These elements were an integral part of Smith's texts and were geared towards emphasizing the idea of human use and facilitating regional comparison.

In many other texts of the early period captions were frequently missing or purely descriptive. Smith was the first to fully use captions to illustrate ideas, pose problems, and to serve as cross references to the material under discussion. Further facility was gained by having figures with page references. This was an excellent device which simplified the location of maps and photographs referred to in the textual material.[55] His early attention to the educational value of carefully planned illustrations and captions added immeasurably to the value of his books.

Smith also recognized the importance of maps as a basic geographic tool and endeavored to arouse interest in them. Primarily his purpose was to create map-mindedness by showing students how maps could heighten the meaning of the text, especially in reference to human use. With

[54]J. Russell Smith, "Suggestion for Illustrating Books," *Annals of the Association of American Geographers*, XXXII (September, 1942), 316.
[55]Smith, "Suggestions for Illustrating Books," p. 316.

this purpose in mind, he included human-use maps[56] along with the standard color and black-and-white physical and political maps. These human-use maps were a new feature in elementary texts. The map idea was consistently presented in a graded, developmental manner, the primary books starting with maps of the home community. Maps were never made ends in themselves, but rather were employed as interesting and useful tools in learning about man and his world. Smith was one of the first textbook writers to have meaningfully captioned maps and to refer to them in the text as a basis for creative pupil activities.

Problems and exercises. Smith always had a generous supply of exercise material in all of his texts as an additional means of developing skill and understanding.[57] However, exercises, too, were never used as ends in themselves but rather as auxiliaries to learning. The questions and exercises were varied, thought provoking, and directly related to the text. They were graded, usually in three levels, to meet the varying abilities of pupils. Many were formulated by school personnel and tested in classroom situations before being incorporated into the books.

Though some of these features were becoming common in the texts of his time, Smith was really the first to so fully emphasize ideas and attitudes in his questions, exercises, activities, and illustrations. A typical example of a question designed to point up attitudes was one at the end of a section on the American Indians. It was: "What do you admire most in the American Indians, and what could they do better than we?"[58]

[56]J. Russell Smith, *Foreign Lands and Peoples* (Philadelphia: The John G. Winston Company, 1933), p. v.

[57]Smith, *Human Geography, Book Two, Regions and Trade,* p. vi.

[58]J. Russell Smith, *World Folks* (Philadelphia: The John C. Winston Company, 1930), p. 15.

Aids for teachers and the necessity for increased professional preparation. Smith was always concerned with teaching method. He realized the predicament of the average, over-burdened teacher who often had a weak background in geography and little time to develop the scholarship necessary for a strong and productive point of view. Smith, therefore, was scrupulous in providing teachers with methods of instruction.

In his texts and in the teacher's manuals accompanying them, he presented the plan of the book, teaching suggestions, and philosophical ideas necessary to implement the texts. Numerous additional questions, activities, supplementary readings, and ideas for developing lesson plans were important features of his geographies. The John C. Winston Company also published copies of Smith's articles on different educational topics for free distribution to teachers.[59] In addition, Smith communicated with teachers through various educational associations and journals. He presented papers before the National Council of Geography Teachers, now the National Council for Geographic Education. Later, these papers were published in the *Journal of Geography.* Other professional journals such as *School Executive* and *Progressive Education* also published some of his educational articles.

Furthermore, Smith did important pioneering work with the World Federation of Educational Associations and the National Society for the Study of Education. In reference to the former, Smith played a prominent part in their 1933 meeting in Dublin, as chairman of the Department of Geography. The theme of the group he chaired was the "mutual appreciation of peoples." He was chosen to head this division, not only because of his wide recog-

---

[59]Smith, *Geography and the Higher Citizenship,* pp. 1–25. This booklet is an excellent example of material designed to aid teachers.

nition as an educator and writer but also because of his
early advocacy of world citizenship and understanding.[60]

In the National Society for the Study of Education, he
was among the active members assisting the Society's
Central Committee on the preparation of the *Thirty-
Second Yearbook,* the theme of which was "The Teaching
of Geography." The resulting book covered all phases of
geography and was a significant guidepost in geographic
education. Smith was specifically connected with the section entitled, "The Development of Geography and its
General Contributions to Life," his article being "How
Geography Contributes to General Ends in Education."[61]

In this yearbook article Smith reiterated the necessity
for a stronger preparation in geography in teacher-training
programs. In addition, he criticized the usual presentation
of geography at the college level with its concentration on
professional preparation and its neglect of general education. He suggested the inclusion of a general survey course
to accommodate the nongeography major.[62] Smith always
believed that such a course should be made a requirement
for all students as a part of their general cultural education. He maintained that this requirement would help to
dispel some of the ignorance of American adults whose
background usually included little geography beyond that
of the old place geography of elementary school.

Smith's texts were written in three main series. In the
early 1920's he wrote *Human Geography* (Book One and
Book Two). His "Single Cycle—Plus Series" occupied him

[60]*Proceedings of the Fifth Biennial Conference of the World Federation of Education Associations* (Dublin, Ireland: World Federation of
Education Associations, 1933).

[61]Smith, "How Geography Contributes to General Ends in Education," pp. 29–42.

[62]*Ibid.,* pp. 29–30. See also Smith, "The Contributions of Economic
Geography to the Preparation of a Teacher of Geography," *Teachers
College Record,* XXX (October, 1929), 356.

during most of the 1930's. In the 1940's he produced the "Our Neighbors Series" with Frank E. Sorenson. Later, this series was finished by Sorenson and Norman Carls. In general, his earlier texts of the 1920's and 1930's showed more originality and creativity than his later ones. This was largely true because at the time when they were written they presented many innovations in the field. It was in these early books that Smith set forth his basic ideas and methods. His later texts were in many ways the reworking or supplementing of the earlier ones.

HUMAN GEOGRAPHY, BOOK ONE AND BOOK TWO

These two books were written on the double-cycle principle, each book covering the entire world once. *Book One, Peoples and Countries* (1921), was suggested for either grades four or five or five and six.[63] The text portrayed the mutual dependence of people through an excellent introductory presentation of "The Eskimo," "Indians of the Great North Woods," and "The Codfishermen," chosen as type studies of how people satisfy their needs in different geographic regions. Then, after devoting a few pages to a consideration of the earth and maps, Smith treated each continent, emphasizing economic and commercial activities in human situations. Examples of the topics covered were: "How Fishing Helped Start Manufacturing," "The Coconut Grower," and "Climbing To The Coffee Plantation." [64] The book showed that Smith understood children as well as geography because of his use of an interesting story form and his presentation of the earth in terms of human activities.

[63]Smith, *Human Geography, Book One, Peoples and Countries,* p. iv.
[64]*Ibid.,* pp. 153–57, 172–76, 200–4.

Book Two, Regions and Trade (1921), was for grades five and six or six and seven. In general, it covered some of the same material, but because of the more advanced level, it presented a more formal regional analysis of all the continents. Built upon the type study approach used in *Book One,* it was the first elementary text to be fully organized around the human-use analysis of natural regions, rather than the traditional political area.

The books were popular; they went through several editions and captured the enthusiasm of both teachers and pupils. It was these two books which really started Smith's revolution in school geography, because they first successfully presented a truly human orientation. They set the basic pattern of his later works, as well as those of his imitators. The critical comments that appeared at the time of their publication were generally enthusiastic. Mendel E. Branom's remarks were a good example. Branom was then a professor at Harris State Teachers College in St. Louis, Missouri, and an author well known in the field of geographic education. Branom pointed out in reference to Smith's *Human Geography, Book One* that:

The various parts of the earth are studied in the light of human activities. The physical factors are happily interwoven with a vital life topic or problem. Many facts are so appealingly presented that the child will want to memorize them. . . .

This book will rank with the best for elementary schools and should meet with hearty response from teachers.[65]

[65]Mendel E. Branom, Review of *Human Geography, Book One, Peoples and Countries* by J. Russell Smith, *Journal of Geography,* XXI (February, 1922), 145.

Branom responded similarly to *Human Geography, Book Two*. In reviewing this text he said:

All teachers of geography who have been emphasizing natural regions will welcome this book. The author has broken away from the traditional method of organizing the content by countries. . . .

The author has met the demand for a book organized on a natural regional basis and dependent on but different from the book for the lower grades. Added to this is a vivid, appealing style.

Smith's Human Geographies are among the best textbooks available for the grades. The books will also be invaluable reference books for all teachers and students of geography.[66]

THE SINGLE CYCLE—"PLUS" SERIES OF THE 1930's

These texts formed a series covering grades three through seven. The five texts of the 1930 series followed a developmental pattern, going consecutively from the familiar to the unknown. The application of the single-cycle plan of organization was an improvement on the double-cycle plan of the earlier texts, since it made for more systematic grading and eliminated repetition.

The single-cycle series, in order of grade level, consisted of *American Lands and Peoples* (1932), a treatment of the Western Hemisphere for grade five, and *Foreign Lands and Peoples* (1933), a study of the Eastern Hemisphere

[66]Mendel E. Branom, Review of *Human Geography, Book Two, Regions and Trade* by J. Russell Smith, *Journal of Geography*, XXII (January, 1923), 40.

for grade six. The "plus" part was *Our Industrial World* (1934),[67] for the seventh grade.

The formal study of the world as represented by these books was preceded by two elementary texts, involving a study of home geography in *Home Folks* (1927),[68] for the third grade, and the type studies of foreign peoples in *World Folks* (1931), for the fourth grade.

Home Folks.

This text for the third grade filled the need for a readiness geography. The book introduced the child to his own country, by presenting him with life in typical communities such as the farm, the village, the town, and the city. It was written in a simple, interesting story form around Jack Reed, an average American boy and his friends and cousins, characters with whom children could identify. Growing out of the narrative were many concepts about crops, products, trade, industries, and physical features. Attitudinal values, such as those leading to community-mindedness, were stressed. The practical application of the book was extended by questions and exercises planned to help the teacher make comparisons between the child's own home community and communities new to him. The book was notable for its facility in presenting in a concrete, interesting manner the basic concepts to be taught at this beginning stage.

The map idea was introduced through clear diagrams based on pictures of the local communities treated in the

[67]J. Russell Smith, *Our Industrial World* (Philadelphia: The John C. Winston Company, 1934).

[68]J. Russell Smith, *Home Folks* (Philadelphia: The John C. Winston Company, 1927).

text. The attractive and meaningful pictures were also specifically prepared for the stories to capture the attention of children.

Zoe A. Thralls[69] keynoted the significance of *Home Folks* when she stated in reference to the book:

After using this book children should have vivid concepts of life in city and county and their interrelationships. . . . Numerous attempts have been made to write a geography textbook for beginners and at last the formula seems to have been discovered. In *Home Folks* Dr. Smith seems to have combined the right ingredients in their proper proportions— material suitable for almost any region, a style vivid, smoothly flowing and interesting, a story with plenty of action even for the most restless youngster.[70]

World Folks

This text for the fourth grade followed naturally from *Home Folks*. Through imaginary journeys of fictional children it introduced the child to typical communities around the world—the equatorial rain forest, the desert's edge, and the Arctic seashore. These and other type areas were chosen by Smith for their interest and geographic significance. The innovation of a primarily climatic, regional orientation was carried over from his Human Geographies. The factual materials aimed at giving a picture of the total way of life as a natural product of the interaction between man and his environment. Emphasis was put on portraying foreign peoples as normal, creative indi-

[69]Zoe A. Thralls is Professor Emeritus of Geography at the University of Pittsburgh as well as the author of elementary geography texts and books on methods of teaching geography.

[70]Zoe A. Thralls, Review of *Home Folks* by J. Russell Smith, *Journal of Geography*, XXVI (March, 1927), 121.

viduals rather than as peculiar strangers. This human approach was in contradistinction to that used by many other authors of the period. For example, Frye, in his *New Geography*, frequently characterized the natives of Africa as "black savages." [71]

In *World Folks* Smith introduced world maps, after having built up a readiness basis in *Home Folks*. The maps, meaningfully captioned, together with the many illustrations, pointed up the idea of human use and the everyday, normal living of foreign people.

American Lands and Peoples

By the fifth grade, a child proceeding in the developmental pattern of Smith's texts had a general overview of the world and was ready for a more detailed, formal study of his own country and its northern and southern neighbors. *American Lands and Peoples* was largely a revision and elaboration of those parts of *Human Geography, Book One,* dealing with the Western Hemisphere. Although an organizing political framework was now used, the treatment, as in *Human Geography,* was one of man's economic use of natural regions in the broad sense of human ecology. At times, political boundaries almost dropped out of sight, since states and countries were used chiefly as convenient points of reference for location and statistics.

The book was characterized by good textual material, numerous maps, and pictures of high quality. These features aided the development of a concrete image on which the child could base definite relationship understandings

[71]Alexis Frye, *New Geography, Book One* (Boston: Ginn and Co., 1921), pp. 3 and 31.

about the United States and the other nations of the
Western Hemisphere.[72]

Smith's approach in this fifth grade text was characteristically varied and interesting. Usually the technique of
an imaginary journey was used to introduce each section
and to unify the whole book around people. For example,
American Lands and Peoples began with a cross-country
trip from Boston to San Francisco.

Another approach Smith frequently employed to introduce regions was that of uniting the past with the present
by means of an introductory historical description of the
area. This was not unique with Smith, but, at the time,
his emphasis on the presentation of historical data to point
up the changes in man's use of the land through scientific
development was relatively new in elementary textbook
writing. Smith's correlation of history and geography was
in keeping with one of his major objectives. As he said in
the introduction to *American Lands and Peoples:*

We study geography today that we may better understand
and utilize the world where we shall live tomorrow—the
future. Because of this fundamental objective of education,
I have laid special emphasis upon underdeveloped resources
and possible lines of future development.[73]

Illustrative of the emphasis on underdeveloped lands was
his treatment of such areas as the Campos of Brazil and
the Peruvian coastal plain. In his revisions of *American
Lands and Peoples* and other texts, Smith constantly
pointed out new scientific discoveries which held promise
of solving man's problems in depressed regions. The main
virtue of *American Lands and Peoples* was the feeling it

[72]L. H. Halverson, Review of *American Lands and Peoples*, by J.
Russell Smith, *Journal of Geography*, XXXII (March, 1932), 224.
[73]Smith, *American Lands and Peoples*, p. iv.

gave for the peoples and lands of the Western Hemisphere, their basic interdependence, and their potential for growth in the future.

Foreign Lands and Peoples

This book dealt with the Eastern Hemisphere and was largely a revision of *Human Geography, Book Two, Regions and Trade*. In order to organize the book on a sound psychological basis, Smith began with areas having simple geographic relationships and then proceeded to more complex adjustments. Thus, he started with the story of the tent-dwelling nomads of the Eurasian land masses, one of the earliest types of human society and a people who eventually migrated to all parts of the Western World. From this historical beginning, the book proceeded to the Mediterranean area, with emphasis on the physical features of the region and their influence on historical and cultural developments. From there, the book continued on to Europe; Eastern and Southeast Asia; Africa, south of the Sahara; Australia, and the Pacific islands. The synthesis provided by the type-study method aided the student in gleaning major ideas and understandings from the great mass of material. For instance, once the dry subtropical type characterizing the Mediterranean region was mastered, it was easier to understand similar areas in South Africa and Australia. The type-study method gave a clarity and unity to Smith's text which was missing in those of many of his contemporaries. Again, a feeling for the people was stressed, especially their problems and how these might be solved, as evidenced in his discussion of tropical diseases in equatorial Africa and China and Japan's difficulty in feeding their people.

Foreign Lands and Peoples and its revisions, like *Amer-*

ican Lands and Peoples, portrayed the increasingly broad perspective of social studies texts. Smith's aim of deepening world understanding became progressively clear-cut and was especially evident in the 1945 revised edition. Here, the treatment of the problems of various countries, such as the need of better government in Iran, which foreshadowed the 1953 revolt, the problem of the Polish Corridor, and the immigration of Chinese into Indo-China were particularly revealing. Especially significant, too, was this edition's supplement entitled "Geography and World War II," [74] which explored some of the long-term geographic, economic, and historical causes of the war and the problems of winning the peace. Smith concluded with his oft repeated belief in international cooperation in all spheres, rooted in the universal support of a world organization, through which nations could work for the well-being of all.

In both *Foreign Lands and Peoples* and its revisions, Smith's growing insistence on pupil research and the building of sound study habits was apparent. He supplied long lists of supplementary reading and his "suggested activities" increasingly emphasized problem solving and active pupil participation. Cross references, the elaboration of interesting details, and the use of a vivid, stimulating approach helped to point up important ideas and attitudes. The pictures, too, aided in enriching the text. They were meaningful, well captioned, and cited in the text. Many were taken by Smith himself during his field trips to Europe, Asia, and the Middle East.

The numerous and varied maps were another strong point. They included standard color and balck-and-white

[74] J. Russell Smith, "Geography and World War II," supplement to *Geography of Europe, Asia, Africa for Elementary Schools* (Philadelphia: The John C. Winston Company, 1945), pp. 1–65.

relief and political maps, climatic maps, world trade maps, and human-use maps. The last were particularly good in showing relationships between geographic factors and patterns of human use. Smith received assistance from J. Paul Goode in compiling maps for many of the texts of the 1930's including *Foreign Lands and Peoples.*

A reviewer aptly pointed out the strengths of *Foreign Lands and Peoples* as follows:

The book is excellent in that it stresses geographic relationships, uses methods that are sound psychologically, develops skills and habits necessary for independent study and fosters sympathetic understandings of how and why the "other half" of the world lives as it does.[75]

The book, however, had several weaknesses. First of all, Smith did not completely follow the principle he enunciated of going from the simple to the more complex cultural pattern. After starting with the nomandic tribes of Central Asia, he took up the lands around the Mediterranean Sea, proceeded to Northwestern Europe and then to the countries of Middle and Eastern Europe. It would have been more psychologically sound to have saved the unit on Northwestern Europe for last, since this region was the most complex on those covered in the European area. The unit on Northwestern Europe could also have served as an introduction to the lands of Southeast Asia, Africa, and Australia, since the nations of Northwestern Europe were the main colonizing powers in these overseas areas.

Smith's treatment of some of the lands overseas also exhibited several shortcomings. For example, in a sense,

[75]Ella M. Wilson, Review of *Foreign Lands and Peoples,* by J. Russell Smith, *Journal of Geography,* XXXIII (May, 1934), 384.

Smith treated Australia somewhat like a "lost continent."
While he had valuable human-use maps for Eurasia and
Africa, he neglected to include one for Australia. Also, his
use of such terminology as "Australia—A Strange Continent" [76] was not geographic and reflected some of the
"wonder book" approach of an earlier period.

In general, too, Smith's treatment of the lands and peoples of Southeast Asia and Africa could have been more
analytical and dynamic. Even in newer editions, such as
those of 1939 and 1942, he did not sufficiently examine the
political, economic, and social changes taking place among
the native populations that have been brought into sudden
and frequently violent contact with twentieth-century
technology and ideas. In later editions,[77] there was only
an inkling of the strong movement after World War II,
in Southeast Asia and Africa, to achieve political, economic, and social independence from European overlords.
Neither was there a full-enough discussion of the possible future roles of these previously subject peoples in the
changing world scene.

Our Industrial World

This book was the "plus" part and capstone of the
series. It was really a reorganized summary of the previous books and Smith's only text on the junior high school
level. In order to show "old facts in new relationships so
as to have unity while avoiding boring repetition," [78]
Smith presented a study of world regions through leading
world industries. He believed that in this way the seventh

[76] Smith, *Foreign Lands and Peoples*, pp. 328–331.
[77] Smith, Geography and World War II, supplement to *Geography
of Europe, Asia, Africa*, pp. 1–65.
[78] Smith, *Our Industrial World*, p. iii.

or eighth year students could not only review old material, but also see more clearly world industries and economic activities in relation to each other and the natural environment. He followed his earlier plan of using world climatic regions in delimiting world industries. To highlight this approach, he included world and regional climatic maps, his text being the first to emphasize these maps on such a scale. In many ways, *Our Industrial World* was a simplified version of his college text, *Industrial and Commercial Geography*.

The text incorporated a large store of information supplemented by a wide variety of pictures, graphs, charts, maps, and sketches. The last unit on communication and trade was intended to synthesize the various regional economic patterns into an interdependent world framework. The text received good reviews, an example of which was as follows: "The text is a really usable one and no doubt will be enjoyed by both teachers and pupils. J. Russell Smith has made a real contribution in writing this text for geography at the junior high school level." [79]

Despite the favorable comment, the book lacked the appeal of the earlier ones. This resulted in large part from the fact that Smith did not fully apply the human principle. The book was oriented around industries rather than, as in the previous texts, around people living in a total human situation where the reader could feel the pulse and color of life.

THE "OUR NEIGHBORS" SERIES

The "Our Neighbors" Series was in part the revision

[79]Anna C. Larson, Review of *Our Industrial World*, by J. Russell Smith, *Journal of Geography*, XXXIV (May, 1935), 216.

and reworking of Smith's texts of the 1930's. They consisted of *Neighbors at Home* (1947), *Neighbors Around the World* (1947), *Neighbors in the Americas* (1948), *Neighbors in the United States and Canada* (1951), and *Neighbors in Latin America* (1951). The first four were written by Smith in collaboration with Frank E. Sorenson. *Neighbors in Latin America* was written by Sorenson, Norman Carls and Margery D. Howarth.

Though the "Our Neighbors" Series followed a pattern similar to that of Smith's previous series, there were important innovations. The newer texts were modern in illustration. The language was more completely presented. Closer attention was given to building reading skills and to establishing sound study habits. Up-to-date scientific inventions and terminology were included. Important, too, was the more clear-cut organization of some of the books. The most significant feature, however, was the increasingly emphatic social studies orientation.

As with Smith's earlier texts, these books also aimed at imparting to the students a residue of big ideas and constructive attitudes that would have lasting meaning for them. Accordingly, facts were used to prepare a framework for ideas and attitudes appropriate to the temper, problems, and needs of current times. Smith's persistent themes of "One World," "International Cooperation," and "World Citzienship" were given heightened importance in this series.

Outstanding, too, was the re-emphasis of geography as the study of relationships and the impact of these relationships on the interdependence of peoples. The word "Neighbors" in all the titles helped to maintain the theme of interdependence. At the same time, correlation with other subject areas received increased attention in keeping with Smith's enlarged cultural approach. The nucleus of Smith's methodology was again the natural, human-use region, with understanding facilitated by personalized explanation, illustration, and comparison in terms of human life. Though written in collaboration with Sorenson, it is apparent from the text that the books were largely Smith's work.

Our Neighbors at Home

Our Neighbors at Home,[80] like its predecessor Home Folks, was for the third grade. However, it was more of a social studies text than the earlier book. Again, the "communityness" of the American way of life was a major theme which expanded into the larger concept of the interdependence of people in family and community life.

This text played a basic psychological role in the series. As Smith pointed out, it was a home geography of the United States as well as a "book of citizenship with social responsibility."[81] By initially establishing the concept of cooperative living in groups with which the young child could identify, a readiness basis was laid for thinking in terms of cooperation in the world community introduced at a higher level. Studies of ten representative or type communities in the United States were given to illustrate the interrelationship between man and his natural environment. The types ranged from "The General Farm Community" and various other agricultural and industrial communities to "The Big City Community." It was pointed out that these communities were alike in some

[80]J. Russell Smith and Frank E. Sorenson, Our Neighbors at Home (Philadelphia: The John C. Winston Company, 1947).

[81]J. Russell Smith, "The Neighbors Series," Unpublished memorandum dated March 4, 1948, p. 4.

ways and different in others depending upon how people used what nature has given them. Despite local differences, however, it was emphasized that we were all Americans.

Like *Home Folks, Neighbors at Home* was written in interesting story form around realistic people and situations. Ideas were introduced relating to basic human needs, industrial and agricultural techniques, and other fundamental geographic concepts, but in a simple, concrete manner as part of the life of the people in the story.

In keeping with Smith's integrated approach, attention was given to developing vocabularly and reading skills. The text of the stories was well suited to the grade level and new terms were defined the first time they were used. A well-organized glossary was also included.

Other aids to understanding and reinforcement of learning were significant in adding value to the text. For example, in order to build basic ideas of trade and commerce, each unit ended with an explanation of how people sold goods in order to get money to purchase what they did not produce. A variety of exercise material was provided at the end of each chapter.

There was also generous use of colored pictures and photographs, as in all of Smith's books. Most illustrations were good, especially the large, interesting, and meaningful photographs. The colored drawings by Geogre G. Whitney were a new addition, since Smith had previously relied on photographs. Most of Whitney's drawings were apt. Some of his close-ups of people, however, so distorted human features that they appeared to be caricatures.[82] Perhaps this this was done to inject humor or realism. If

[82]M. Melvina Svec, Review of *Our Neighbors at Home,* by J. Russell Smith and Frank E. Sorenson, *Journal of Geography,* XLVII (November, 1948), 336.

so, the drawings were too sophisticated and out-of-place at this grade level. Also, some of Whitney's illustrations seemed to contradict the text. For example, on Page 201, the workers appeared to be fighting with each other to get on a bus while the text played up cooperation. Then, too, as on page 181, some of the drawings seemed to have specific national groups working at specific jobs, rather than a generalized type.

In the later edition of 1954, changes were made in the drawings which brought them up to the usual high standard of Smith's texts. The many good features of the book helped atone for the early deficiencies.

Neighbors Around the World

The second book in the series was *Neighbors Around the World*[83] for the fourth grade. Though like *World Folks* in general plan, it was more completely an introductory global geography. Unit I, "Our Globe," aimed at orienting the student to a world view in addition to giving him the basic concepts of mathematical geography and the global map. These new and relatively abstract concepts were presented in Smith's inimitable story form. The central figure was "Sam Tyler" who accompanied his father to Greenland where the latter had charge of a weather station. Through his trip, "Sam" learned about the polar-lands, weather and climate, the polar air route, and the world's land masses and water bodies. Excellent global maps were included, drawn by Dr. Herbert A. Bauer, cartographer, geographer, and artist.

After the introductory overview, the authors presented

[83]J. Russell Smith and Frank E. Sorenson, *Neighbors Around the World* (Philadelphia: The John C. Winston Company, 1947).

a series of type studies representing the major world climatic areas and their characteristic human-use patterns. All major land types were included such as the desert regions, the tropical grasslands, and the equatorial forests. At all times emphasis was put on man's use of the region in which he lived. In strengthening the global concept, it was gradually shown that natural types created similarities in man's adjustment patterns in different parts of the world.

Again, Smith's interesting style helped make the book. Such stories as those about the little Eskimo boy Ahpellah and his family were illustrative of Smith's characteristically meaningful and motivational approach. Important, too, was the attention given to building sound attitudes such as the need for conservation, world cooperation, and good citizenship.

There were many good illustrations in addition to well-formulated, graded questions, exercises, and activities which facilitated the learning of concepts and attitudes.[84] The texts also included a fairly well-developed index and glossary.

The chief weakness of the book lay in Smith's approach to the evolving life of the people in underdeveloped areas, especially those that were or till recently had been part of colonial empires. He did not go deeply enough into the present, nor project sufficiently into the future in discussing the changes taking place in the rapidly developing areas of Asia and Africa. For example, he told of the African people attending school, wearing European clothing and learning new skills. However, the changes have been deeper and more dramatic than these alone

[84]M. Melvin Svec, Review of *Neighbors Around the World*, by J. Russell Smith, *Journal of Geography*, XLVII (November, 1948), 337.

represent. In many ways, he treated the people of these areas in a rather stereotyped manner, at times in the vein of the nineteenth century concept of natives as simple children of the forest. There was not enough emphasis on the high degree of political, economic, and social consciousness which, in recent years, has lead to strong anti-colonial movements as well as to the establishment of independent native states.

The illustrations though numerous and interesting also had a static quality. They emphasized the old village life which, though still important except perhaps in China, was far from being the whole pattern. For example, next to a picture of the simple Congo village there should have been one of a bustling street in Leopoldville. Both are basic facets of life in this and similar areas, but the latter perhaps points more directly to the future. If children are to receive a full understanding of the interplay between man and his total environment, the full impact of the twentieth century must be shown even at the fourth grade level.

Neighbors in the Americas

This book[85] for the fifth grade dealt with the countries of the Western Hemisphere. Here again, the book was written largely in story form and treated areas in reference to land type and use rather than artificial political divisions. Regional geography approached in this manner provided a greater opportunity for students to obtain a clear understanding of man in relation to his environment. This human-use, regional organization was also basic to

[85] J. Russell Smith and Frank E. Sorenson, *Neighbors in the Americas* (Philadelphia: The John C. Winston Company, 1948).

Smith's emphasis on conceptual learning. A good example
was his discussion of factors that made a city[86] and the
classification of cities into major types. Thus, instead of
presenting more than a hundred American cities as separate entities, the cities were studied within an organized
frame of reference.

In addition to an ideational approach, the emphasis on
the teaching of attitudes was in constant evidence. Thus,
the "Good Neighbor Policy" was an important theme
together with world cooperation and good will. The stories
heightened these attitudes by attempting to initiate understanding of the problems, limitations, potentialities, hopes,
and fears accompanying the human struggle to live and
earn a living in the different lands of the Americas.
Smith pointed out that a feeling of cooperation should not
be limited to the Western Hemisphere but should char-
acterize world relations. Every opportunity was also taken
to engender an understanding of the need for the conservation of natural resources. Told in relation to the interesting stories of realistic people, the great importance
of conservation to each nation's life became acutely
meaningful.

The social studies orientation of the text was heightened
by the renewed correlation of geography and history and
the emphasis on social living. A varied approach helped
to sharpen interest, stimulated mental impressions, and
clinched significant concepts. The creative exercises and
thought questions served a similar function, as did the
well-chosen illustrations.

In general, the maps were good. In keeping with the
more advanced grade level, they were more numerous
and varied. There were physical-political, isobaric-

[86]Smith and Sorenson, *Neighbors in the Americas,* pp. 90–1.

hachure, and physiographic maps. Outline and dot maps were used to show specific information. Two types of supplementary maps were especially noteworthy. One was a black outline map of the United States with the white overprint designed to show relationships. The other was the products map of which there were twenty-two varieties. On each map, the equator was the line of orientation in order to facilitate comparisons between latitude, temperature, and plant growth.

The main weakness of the text was its lack of balance in the presentation of material. The unequal page weight of the different regions belied the book's title. Of the 372 pages, 61 were devoted to North America exclusive of the United States, 188 to the United States and her possessions and 96 to South America. In reality, therefore, the book was a geography of the United States. Smith tried to cover too wide a scope with the result that the other areas of North and South America were rather sketchily presented. Thus, the student might have come away with a good understanding of the United States, but without enough insights into the patterns of life in other areas of the Western Hemisphere.

Neighbors in the United States and Canada[87]

This text helped rectify some of the organizational imperfections of Neighbors in the Americas. Since the former book covered only the northern lands of the Western Hemisphere, it offered a more comprehensive and better organized study of the area. Smith did not treat South

[87]J. Russell Smith and Frank E. Sorenson, Neighbors in the United States and Canada (Philadelphia: The John C. Winston Company, 1951).

America, since this region was covered in *Neighbors in Latin America*.[88] *Neighbors in the United States and Canada* was one of the best-written and popular texts in the series. North America was Smith's area of specialization and his interest, enthusiasm, and knowledge of the subject were apparent in his last major contribution to textbook writing. There seemed to be added intensity and vitality in his message: "There are two things for which every one of us should be very watchful if we wish our country to prosper. One is to *keep our freedom,* and the other is to *save our resources.*" [89]

The book was rich in maps, graphs, charts, and excellent illustrations. Special maps and charts gave a profusion of information about such things as the distribution of raw materials and industries, farm crops, the human-use pattern of various regions, and special land-use programs such as the Central Valley Project.[90]

Other important features were a comprehensive section on statistics, a pronouncing index, and a well-chosen, appended atlas containing sixteen additional maps. These maps included global, regional, political, and climatic representations to facilitate the building of relationship concepts. The maps were the combined efforts of Dr. Hubert A. Bauer and Colin Landin. Map skills were introduced early in the text and applied throughout.

The study exercises grouped under the headings "Something to Do" and "A Short Quiz" were varied and meaningful. They aided reinforcement of textual learnings through their emphasis on understanding and practical

[88]Norman Carls, Frank E. Sorenson, and Margery D. Howarth, *Neighbors in Latin America* (Philadelphia: The John C. Winston Company, 1951).

[89]Smith and Sorenson, *Neighbors in the United States and Canada,* p. iv.

[90]*Ibid.,* pp. vi–viii.

application. A good example was the following activity which stated, "Look for a place near your school where the soil has been washed or blown away. See if you can discover where this soil goes." [91]

Smith's story form again generated anticipation and interest. A general overview was provided by a quick plane trip across the United States. Then Alaska and Canada were treated before the detailed regional study of the United States was begun. By using this psychological approach Smith first introduced some general concepts about North America and thus provided a readiness basis for the more complex regional analysis of the United States which followed.

In general the book was well received. A typical reaction was as follows:

There is a certain flare in the writing of this text which demands the attention of the reader. A wealth of information points up the relationship between man's use of the land and the nature of the land itself. The writers not only achieve geographic understandings in developing this book; there is a definite plan for developing reading skills and abilities.[92]

Despite the good features of the text, there were some shortcomings. To a large extent, the book was based on old material. Except for some new statistics and other data, the text itself was almost a verbatim copy of Unit I ("The United States" and Unit II ("Canada") of *Neighbors in the Americas*. The only really new material consisted of the additional maps, charts, and pictures. There was no justification for so little modification in a sup-

[91]*Ibid.*, p. 279.
[92]Annice Davis Elkins, Review of *Neighbors in the United States and Canada*, by J. Russell Smith and Frank E. Sorenson, *Journal of Geography*, XLVII (September, 1949), 260.

posedly new text, even if the earlier material was basically sound.

Then, too, the problem of organization still persisted. Improvements had been made but again there was a lack of balance. Of the 323 pages, only 43 were devoted to Canada. Thus, the book was really another geography of the United States with insufficient attention given to other northern lands of the Western Hemisphere. One of Smith's major themes was the importance of developing a spirit of cooperation and friendship between the United States and Canada. However, he spent so little time on Canada that only vague generalities, rather than real understandings, could be formed.

Organization could also have been improved by placing Alaska within the unit on the United States rather than in Unit II, "The Northlands," which included Canada. Although just recently made a state, Alaska has long been an important territory of the United States. It was strange, too, that there was no mention of Alaska's possible change in status. Nor was any real connection made between Alaska's strategic position and wealth of resources and their effect on the future of the United States.

A similar lack of long-range analysis was present in the regional delineation of certain parts of the United States, especially New England and the South. There was not enough emphasis on the evolving economic patterns of each region and the eventual cultural and political implications of these changes. The new industrial revolution in the South and the migration of some of New England's heavy industries to other areas should have been more than just suggested.

It is significant that after almost forty years Smith's texts are still leaders in the elementary field. It indicates that he had a real understanding of how to make geography interesting and meaningful, so as to capture the attention and imagination of children. This accomplished, he hoped to make the ideas and attitudes embodied in his books an integral part of the spirit and actions of the students reading them, in keeping with the objectives of the "higher citizenship."

VII

Smith's Work in Applied Geography

SMITH DEMONSTRATED THE DYNAMIC AND PRACTICAL NATURE of geography through his activities in applying geographic principles to contemporary problems and issues as well as through his teaching and the preparation of textbooks. These activities included his work and writings resulting from World War I, his writings in relation to the Depression, and his practical field experiments and writings in conservation and plant genetics. These activities were not lucrative. Smith was motivated by his own interest in and awareness of urgent problems that needed to be attacked by long-range, scientific planning.

SMITH'S WORK STEMMING FROM WORLD WAR I

Smith, although a Quaker and an internationalist, engaged in projects connected with the war effort of 1917–1918. In attacking various wartime problems he was able to use much of the training and experience gained through his work in geography and applied fields.

158

Smith's Activities in Food and
Agricultural Programs

Smith actively participated in local community activities, particularly those in connection with food and agricultural programs. In April, 1917, a committee on agricultural service was formed at the University of Pennsylvania. Smith was elected chairman and in two weeks' time had three hundred boys working as farm volunteers in various states.[1] From April, 1917, to November, 1917, Smith served as chairman of both the Food Commission of the Philadelphia School Mobilization Committee and the Food Section of the Mayor's Home Defense Committee.[2] During this time, he ran active newspaper campaigns on food conservation and market reporting. In addition, he participated in many food and clothing drives of the American Friends' Service Committee.

Smith's Writings Related to Food Supply
and Allied Problems

Smith's activities were not limited to organizational work. He wrote numerous articles about wartime problems. In 1917, three of his articles appeared in the influential farm magazine *Country Gentleman*. These urged the organization and launching of a national food con-

[1]"War Services of the Members of the Association of American Geographers," *Annals of the Association of American Geographers,* IX (1919), 67. See also an undated memorandum of Smith listing his activities in World War I.
[2]*Ibid.,* p. 67.

servation campaign.[3] They were widely reprinted. In the same year, *Review of Reviews*[4] published articles by Smith. One urged the organization of sound international machinery for peace.[5] The other called for a national campaign for increased shipbuilding.[6] *Century*[7] also published several of Smith's articles. One dealt with national policy regarding the control of industry in war and stressed the use of a selective draft.[8] Other articles treated the problem of an adequate food supply and the difficulty of meeting the needs of a world at war.[9]

In November, 1917, the Carnegie Endowment for International Peace requested Smith to make a detailed study of the effects of the war on shipping. The result was a detailed report of 347 pages, completed in June, 1918, entitled, *The Influence of the Great War on Shipping*.[10] The chief point that Smith made in his report was that the war had made the United States the chief trading nation of the world; and, as a result, we had to formulate positive trading policies that would lead to economic internationalism.

[3]The three articles referred to are: "Shall the World Starve?" *Country Gentleman*, LXXXII (June 9, 1917), 3–4, 24; "Why We Hate the Food Speculator," *Country Gentleman*, LXXXII (June 23, 1917), 1–2; "Quit Fooling and Talk Sense," *Country Gentleman*, LXXXII (August 4, 1917), 4–5, 28.

[4]*Review of Reviews* is no longer in existence but at the time was a monthly periodical of commentary on national and international affairs.

[5]J. Russell Smith, "Neutralized World," *Review of Reviews*, LVI (August, 1917), 170–71.

[6]J. Russell Smith, "Building Ships to Beat the Submarines," *Review of Reviews*, LVI (October, 1917), 393.

[7]*Century*, no longer in existence, was an influential and popular monthly periodical.

[8]J. Russell Smith, "The Selective Draft in Industry," *Century*, XCIV (September, 1917), 137–42.

[9]J. Russell Smith, "Next Year's Food," *Century*, XCIV (August, 1917), 633; "Food or Famine," *Century*, XCIV (September, 1917), 685–89.

[10]J. Russell Smith, *The Influence of the Great War on Shipping* (Washington, D. C.: Carnegie Endowment for International Peace, 1918).

Soon after completing the report for the Carnegie Foundation, Smith was granted a year's leave from the Wharton School to become a special trade expert in the Bureau of Research of the War Trade Board in Washington. He was chosen for the position because of his work and writings in international trade. Until January, 1919, he was in charge of the preparation of miscellaneous reports on shipping facilities and favorable trade routes.

Writings Resulting from Postwar Problems

As a result of his war experience, three problems concerning the future of the postwar world occupied Smith's thinking. They were: (1) the nature of American trade after the war; (2) the establishment of world cooperation in order to keep the peace; and (3) the production of food resources sufficient to feed a hungry world.

In reference to the question of postwar trade, Smith wrote in 1919 "The American Trade Balance and Probable Trade Tendencies." [11] It embodied an analysis of the foreign trade of the United States during the years immediately preceding 1919 and advanced some ideas as to its future course. Smith pointed out that the war had become a leading exporter to a pleading world that had previously been largely supplied by Europe.[12] Many Americans believed that we would retain this lead. Smith believed, however, that after the war Europe would regain her former supremacy or perhaps even surpass it, because of mass production, the more widespread use of agri-

[11]J. Russell Smith, "The American Trade Balance and Probable Trade Tendencies," *Annals of the American Academy of Political and Social Science*, LXXXIII (May, 1919), 86–105.
[12]This article was first published in pamphlet form by the National Foreign Trade Council in April, 1919.

cultural machinery, and improved industrial organization. According to Smith, our adjustment to this harsh reality "will be the greatest single reconstruction that America faces—reconstruction of her foreign trade." [13] Smith's predictions largely came true. Instead of answering the reborn competition with international agreements, the United States followed a policy of economic isolationism maintained by some of the highest tariffs in her history.

Smith's realization of the fundamental relation between world peace and international economic cooperation was evident in another of his articles entitled "Trade and a League of Nations or Economic Internationalism," [14] in which he dealt specifically with the economic cause of war. The most important causes to him were interference with the trade of other nations through transit restrictions, the exclusion of people who wished to emigrate, concessions for foreign investments, interference with trade by tariffs, and most-favored-nation clauses. Though he supported the League of Nations, he criticized its policy of encouraging nationalism and particularism which to him were "dynamite . . . as long as one people has much greater opportunity per man in its territory than a neighboring people has." [15] He pointed out that modern world conditions had made all peoples neighbors, whether they liked it or not. He was prophetic when he said, "Taking the long view, we may perhaps say that the greatest menace to permanent world peace lies in the Pacific, where we see love of racial particularism causing the white peoples of the United States, British Columbia,

[13]Smith, "The American Trade Balance and Probable Trade Tendencies," p. 104.
[14]J. Russell Smith, "Trade and a League of Nations or Economic Internationalism," *Annals of the American Academy of Political and Social Science*, LXXXIII (May, 1919), 287–306.
[15]*Ibid.*, p. 289.

and Australia to exclude the Chinese." [16] He similarly
made a plea for the "open door," free trade, and, in sum,
economic internationalism. As Smith had feared, the
League's inability to check the basic economic causes of
war led to the Second World War, in 1939.

Another important publication during the postwar
period was *The World's Food Resources*.[17] The book was
pertinent and timely. The World War, which necessitated
the withdrawal of thousands of ships from their usual
routes, brought into sharp focus the dangerous problem
of food shortage. Conditions showed how far society
had traveled from the days when a family could be supplied from its own acres. In the twentieth century, nations
supplied nations in ever-widening circles of interdependence. The war had convinced Smith that a major issue of
the war, and to a great extent that of the peace, lay in
the question of food supply. Through an exhaustive study
of all materials that were serving or could possibly serve
as human nourishment, Smith attempted to answer the
following major question in his book: "Has food shortage
come to stay, or is there a bounteous future ahead of us?"[18]

Again, he sought a solution by linking the world's food
problem to the basic attitudes of people. If men co-
operatively developed the earth's resources for the good
of all, food could be had in abundance in this age of
science. If their chief concern was conquest of each other,
then millions of the world's people faced ultimate starva-
tion and death.[19] Smith believed that the concomitant
essential to world cooperation was economic and social
justice within a country. Quite frequently food scarcity

was the result of an archaic and autocratic system built on the unequal distribution of goods, wealth, and land. Thus, *The World's Food Resources*, to an extent, was again a plea for internationalism and economic justice as prerequisites to solving the age-old scourge of mankind, that of famine and want.[20]

Smith was optimistic about man's ability to increase the food supply in order to provide all people with a minimum standard of living. The modern world had many devices at hand to increase food resources. Science had made possible and would further make possible the reclaiming of unused lands, the use of new machine processes, scientific agriculture, rapid transportation, and better methods of food conservation and distribution.

In *The World's Food Resources* Smith gave numerous examples of acreage in all continents which he believed had possibilities for development. For example, he pointed out the extensive swamplands in different parts of the United States and laid special emphasis on the proposal current after World War I for the systematic draining of the marshlands of the South. He considered these undeveloped acres to be among our greatest reserves of cheap, unused land. He similarly drew attention to the thousands of square miles of dry lands in the West that he felt could be made productive by irrigation. Other examples in North America were the vast plains west of Winnipeg, Canada, and the luxuriant grass and grain lands of Alaska that could make this region a new Finland. Many areas of South America, Africa, Australia, and New Zealand also offered much promise of development. The recent plan of the Argentine government, announced in

[20]Among others of the *avant garde* of the time who urged international cooperation were: James T. Shotwell, Tasker H. Bliss, David Hunter Miller, and Joseph P. Chamberlain.

1959, for the utilization of the mineral and grazing wealth of Patagonia, called a wasteland by Charles Darwin, is an indication of what Smith meant. Many similar projects have come to pass or are in a stage of development in areas of the world that Smith indicated in this book as having potential.

It is particularly interesting to see what Smith said about the then young U.S.S.R. and China. He stated that the trans-Siberian railroad had opened up a country with a wide belt of potential grain and mineral lands. He believed this might permit the Russians to increase greatly their agricultural production. Russia's present-day awareness of the potential of her vast Asiatic frontier is clearly seen in her current Seven Year Plan. This plan has about 40 per cent of the U.S.S.R.'s expenditures geared to the development of Eastern Siberia and other frontier areas.

Smith believed that because of China's huge labor supply and unused mineral resources, her manufacturing possibilities were perhaps greater than those of the United States.[21] He considered her unused agricultural resources to be extensive, requiring only modern methods for development. This line of thinking is also that of the current Chinese Communist regime.

Thus, Smith believed that modern science was the key to growth and development in all phases of economic activity, since "science creates resources of value to every land." [22] Smith was especially emphatic about the importance of scientific agriculture for any long-range gains in the food supply. By the use of soil conservation practices, new chemical fertilizers, and plant genetics many significant strides could be made. Further application of improvements in food conservation, transportation, and

[21]Smith, *The World's Food Resources,* p. 183.
[22]*Ibid.,* p. 321.

distribution would permit a fuller use of agricultural resources that were often wasted. These were but a few of the many items that Smith suggested. As he pointed out, however, time and long-range planning were needed to bring all these factors into play.

The book was a "very valuable contribution to geographic and economic literature." [23] In addition to its social message, it was one of the most extensive studies at the time of the world's food supply and the possibilities for future development. Primarily, though, as Smith pointed out, in a well-fed world, there might be fewer of the tension-producing factors that often breed war.

SMITH AND THE DEPRESSION YEARS

Characteristically, Smith actively struck out against the problems besetting the United States during the Depression period. He participated in the various aid campaigns of the Society of Friends and wrote widely in *The Friends' Intelligencer,* a leading Quaker magazine.

As chairman of the subcommittee of the All Friends Conference of 1935, he guided the preparation of a pamphlet entitled *Methods of Achieving Economic Justice.*[24] It was subtitled "A syllabus for those concerned to act in the light of knowledge." Its text and annotated bibliography dealt with such items as scarcity economics in the midst of abundance, a declining standard of living, and America's capacity to produce and consume. Its aim was to provide information on these and other topics and to present a program that Quakers and those of like mind

[23]O. D. Von Engeln, "The World's Food Resources," *Geographical Review,* VIII (December, 1919), 170.
[24]J. Russell Smith, *et al., Methods of Achieving Economic Justice* (Purcellville, Va.: Blue Ridge Herald Press, 1935).

could follow. Among the important points that Smith and his fellow committeemen advocated were economic internationalism, a decent minimum standard of living, self-help cooperatives, a decrease in federal regulation, and a weakening of the power of the rich through stricter anti-trust laws and increased taxation. Smith and the other contributors maintained that big business needed reorganization in the form of more ethical practices, scientific management, and a de-emphasis on the profit motive, in order to bring about a greater degree of social justice. The pamphlet was particularly critical of the government's policy of scarcity economics which Smith believed caused hunger and want in a land immensely rich in natural resources and industrial potential.

Smith was also a member of the subcommittee of the Committee on Unemployment and Industrial Stabilization of the National Progressive Conference, which was formed to try to deal with the problems of the Depression. The report, which Smith and other members of the subcommittee prepared, put emphasis on the necessity for experimental, long-range, collective planning on the national level. It was further proposed that a National Economic Board be established, composed of experts in finance, scientific management, labor relations, economics, and agriculture,[25] which would plan a program for maintaining and increasing production rather than limiting it.

The fundamental questions of scarcity economics and government regulation were again the themes of Smith's later book, The Devil of the Machine Age.[26] The depression saw the extreme irony of hunger in the midst of

[25]J. M. Clark, J. Russell Smith, Edwin S. Smith, and George Soule, "Long-Range Planning for the Regularization of Industry," New Republic, LXIX (January 13, 1932), 3–23.
[26]J. Russell Smith, The Devil of the Machine Age (New York: Harcourt, Brace and Company, 1941).

plenty, of enormous, untapped markets, adjacent to equally large productive power, and of buyer and seller unable to carry on their normal affairs because the buyers could not pay for the things they needed. The machine age had created abundance, but at the same time also the attendant fear that large supplies would deflate prices. The "devil," Smith said was the fallacious doctrine of scarcity in order to keep prices high, on which the whole world economic structure was being built.[27] By following this doctrine he feared that the country would go from bad to worse in the direction of poverty, inequality, oppression, complete government control, general social disruption and perhaps even war.

Smith was highly critical of the temporary devices of the New Deal, such as limited production goals, price fixing, wage stabilization, federal subsidies, nonproductive W.P.A. projects, doles, plowing under, government payments for failure to produce, and pump priming. He described these measures only as a succession of "idiocies" perpetrated by bankers, industrialists, merchants, farmers, and virtually all classes and sections of society for the purpose of establishing scarcity.[28] Instead, Smith advocated in *The Devil of the Machine Age* an economy of abundance in which the country and the world might learn to stabilize itself in terms of the resources which the world as a whole could provide.[29]

In place of the scarcity system where "everybody is trying to get better off at the expense of everybody else," [30] he wished to see more harmonious social and economic system. Therefore, he again proposed consumers' cooperatives, producers' cooperatives, consumer organizations for

[27]*Ibid.*, pp. 3–7.
[28]*Ibid.*, pp. 37–41.
[29]*Ibid.*, pp. 83–84.
[30]*Ibid.*, p. 88.

protection, private business run for a regulated fair profit, government operation of some enterprises such as public utilities, and nonprofit private foundations. Although some of his remedies may seem overidealized, his advocacy of an economy of abundance was considered by many to be fundamentally sound. Looking at the situation realtisically, he believed that American businessmen faced an ultimate choice. They could make an economy of abundance within a reasonable profit system and on an ethical social order, or else they might end up one day handing over all business to the government.[31] Smith had seen depression bring state socialism to Germany, Italy, and Russia; and he feared that America's freedom was at stake. As he said in his concluding sentence, "Will it take bombs to make us face facts?" [32] In general, the book was well received as a direct and succinct analysis of the controversial economic policies of the Depression period.[33]

SMITH'S WORK IN CONSERVATION

Smith's lifelong work in conservation and related fields reflected his deep-rooted love of the land. Some might even consider his work in this area to be his greatest contribution.

Conservation and Tree Crops,
The Problem and the Aim

The major theme of Smith's work and writings in con-

[31]*Ibid.*, p. 87.
[32]*Ibid.*, p. 89.
[33]See especially the following reviews for critical comments: T. P. Boland, *Commonweal*, XXXIV (June 6, 1941), 162; Keith Hutchinson, *Nation*, CLII (April 19, 1941), 476; R. G. Woolbert, *Foreign Affairs*, XX (January, 1942), 376.

servation and plant genetics was the use of crop trees as a means of preventing and curing the ravages of erosion on steep, rocky, or dry lands, while at the same time providing valuable fodder for animals and food for man.[34] Although his full appreciation of the value of crop-bearing trees did not come until his experiments on his own farm, he was conscious from his childhood of the ravages of erosion.[35] On his father's farm in the steep and rolling Blue Ridge country, the problem of the gully had been real. He had early come to hate this sign of soil ruin. As he said in retrospect, "The sight of a burnt forest hurts me. The sight of a gully hurts me still more, because the damage by the gully is more or less irrevocable in this geological epoch.[36]

His awareness of the ruin and poverty attendant upon the deforestation and erosion of land was heightened over the years by his trips to such areas as western China, Syria, Palestine, Greece, and many regions of the United States. Upon returning from his trip to the Mediterranean in 1913, where he had been looking for crop trees, he commented sadly on those regions which had been misused by man. In *Tree Crops* he said:

Syria is an even more deplorable example than China. Back of Antioch, in a land that was once as populous as rural Illinois, there are now only ruin and desolation. The once prosperous Roman farms now consist of wide stretches of bare rock, whence every vestige of soil has been removed by rain.[37]

Smith stressed examples of the proper utilization of

[34]J. Russell Smith, *Tree Crops* (New York: Harcourt, Brace and Company, 1929), p. 189.
[35]Interview with Professor Smith, July 14, 1953.
[36]Interview with Professor Smith, July 14, 1953.
[37]Smith, *Tree Crops*, (1929), p. 9.

hill land which he had seen on the same Mediterranean trip, such as the two-story Majorca farms where the olive, fig, or oak were planted on the hillsides.[38] Beneath the fig and olive trees crops of wheat, clover, and chick-peas were regularly rotated. Beneath the oaks grazed the pigs that harvested and grew fat from the rich crop of acorns. The hillside lands were intact and after hundreds of years of use were still producing. Thus Smith came to understand that the knowledge and attitude of the people could influence, to a large extent, the ruin or prosperity of a region.

The great degree of soil waste in the United States made him fear for the economic future of this country. He maintained that "without any doubt, the American is the most destructive animal that ever trod the earth." [39] He cited alarming statistics to substantiate his opinion, such as the fact that, after a relatively short period of settlement, nearly 25 per cent of our crop land or one hundred million acres was being damage at a rapid rate of erosion.[40] On the parts of this land that were steep and rolling, the process of water erosion had been hastened by the destructive application of the plow and corn cultivation. Smith warned that, if Americans did not start conservation farming on a wide scale, these acres and millions of others being eroded at a slower rate would be permanently damaged.[41] It was the urgency of this need and his love of trees and the land that prompted his work.[42]

[38]*Ibid.*, 2d ed., Revised (New York: The Devin-Adair Company, 1953), p. 8.
[39]*Ibid.*, p. 5.
[40]*Ibid.*, p. 7.
[41]*Ibid.*, p. 8.
[42]J. Russell Smith, "Nut Tree Crops as a Part of Permanent Agriculture Without Plowing," Northern Nut Growers Association, *Report of Fifteenth Annual Meeting* (New York City, 1924), 103.

Sunny Ridge

Smith's farm at Sunny Ridge was suitable for the experimental study of tree agriculture because it was situated on the rocky slopes of the Blue Ridge. It was near Purcellville and Round Hill, Virginia, not far from where he was born. He bought the 130 acre farm in 1900 as a place to vacation, write, and study.[43] The good stands of black walnut and chestnut were one of the features that attracted him. By the time he sold the farm in 1951, his holdings had expanded to two thousand acres, planted to more than one hundred varieties of nut and other crop trees.[44] These trees, many of which he had bred himself, supported pastures for sheep, pigs, and cattle.

Through the years, his work attracted many people to Sunny Ridge. Among them were soil and tree specialists, conservationists, and just plain farmers who wanted to improve their land. Smith worked closely with all who showed an interest.

The Northern Nut Growers Association and Other Groups

One of the organizations that Smith found most helpful in his work was the Northern Nut Growers Association in which he was particularly active until the 1950's. This unique society was founded in 1910 "to promote interest in nut-producing plants, their products, and their cul-

[43]Interview with Myra Light, secretary to Professor Smith, July 15, 1953.

[44]Letter to the writer from H. L. Crane, Principal Horticulturist of the Horticultural Crops Research Branch of the Agricultural Research Service of the United States Department of Agriculture, Beltsville, Maryland, November 10, 1955.

ture." [45] The membership was open to all interested in nut trees and included tree lovers from all walks of life. Smith joined the group in 1913 to learn new methods of grafting walnuts. He considered their activities so valuable that he became an active member and in 1916 was elected president.[46] The proceedings of their meetings tell much of what Smith was doing at Sunny Ridge, since he invariably read a paper before meetings of the group.

Smith was also interested in the American Genetics Association. He occasionally wrote for their publication, *The Journal of Heredity* and ran several nut tree contests with their cooperation.

In general, government agencies neglected tree crops. However, two experiment stations of the United States Department of Agriculture are worthy of note for their creative work. One is the Horticultural Research Branch at Beltsville, Maryland,[47] and the other is the Southeast Experiment Station at Waseca, Minnesota.[48] Smith worked closely with specialists at these stations.

Tree Farming at Sunny Ridge

Smith's farm was far from being merely a hobby or an intellectual experiment. He ran it along business lines, according to principles of scientific farm management to make it self-sustaining and thus demonstrate that tree-crop

[45]Northern Nut Growers Association, *Report of Second Annual Meeting* (Ithaca, New York, 1911), p. 5.

[46]Northern Nut Growers Association, *Report of Seventh Annual Meeting* (Washington, D. C., 1916), p. 58.

[47]H. L. Crane, Principal Horticulturist, and C. F. Gravatt, Senior Plant Pathologist of the Section of Fruit and Nut Crops, worked closely with Smith.

[48]R. E. Hodgson, Superintendent of the Waseca Experimental Station, often corresponded with Smith.

farming could be a sound investment. As he wrote to his son Stewart who later took over management of the farm:

Farming is a business and it is conducted on either of two systems: the peasant system or a scientific system. . . . I am hoping that thee will be able to follow the golden mean of being a business man and a scientific farmer, as well as a human being.[49]

In order to make his tree crop experiment pay, Smith realized that he had faced a twofold task: finding and breeding the best trees, and developing means of growing them in a scientific and economical manner. Smith searched for the best parent trees on his travels and sought information from individuals and organizations working in the field. He was always on the alert for something better. When he heard of an interesting tree, he would either go to see it or write to the owner, as in the following letter:

I understand from my friend, D. C. Snyder, that you are the owner of the hickory tree that is the parent tree of the variety known as the Cedarapids which a number of us are testing experimentally.

I should very much like to know the history of the parent tree; its age, how regularly it bears, and whether or not the nuts are particularly prized locally—enough, for example, to bring a price above the average.

I hope you will send me two or three pounds. Please let me know the price.[50]

---

[49]Letter from Professor Smith to his son Stewart, March 30, 1931.
[50]Letter from Professor Smith to Edward Siechert, a farmer of Cedar Rapids, Iowa, October 28, 1932.

Smith also conducted contests either on his own or in conjunction with organizations, in order to find superior scions and to awaken interest in crop trees. He publicized the contests extensively by writing to agriculture departments of colleges, local farm journals, and newspapers.[51] These contests were frequently fruitful in finding new and better varieties of trees. As a result of the oak contests of the 1920's, higher acorn-yielding species were found.[52] Walnut contests in 1931 and 1932 provided much information for the Northern Nut Growers Association, which was then attempting to build a new industry around these trees as well as the hickory.[53] Smith's largest number of contests were those for the honey locust, which he ran periodically from the 1920's until World War II. The first contest brought in pods with 25 per cent sugar. Later ones brought in record beans analyzing as high as 35 per cent sugar. The wide range of the trees from the deep South to as far north as southern Minnesota was also discovered.[54]

By using one device or another, Smith usually found a promising tree. He then proceeded to test or hybridize it. If the result was good, he grafted numerous seedlings, planted some in his own orchards and put the rest up for sale in his Sunny Ridge Nursery. He developed this commercial nursery to help defray expenses of the farm and

[51]Letter from Professor Smith to the Editor of the *Valley Farmer*, Portsmouth, Ohio, September 6, 1926. Pertinent also are copies of letters to the *Prairie Home, Country Home,* and the *Missouri Farmer*.

[52]See circulars on contests for the burr oak, the white oak, and the chestnut oak.

[53]J. Russell Smith, "Double-Topworking Hickory Trees," Northern Nut Growers Association, *Report of Twenty-Third Annual Meeting* (Washington, D. C., September, 1932), pp. 115–17.

[54]J. Russell Smith, "Tree Crops, An Unappreciated Possibility," *Bio-Dynamics*, III (Summer, 1943), 38. See also a letter from Professor Smith to the Editor of *Prairie Farmer*, Chicago, Illinois, August 17, 1937.

to publicize his work. Often he gave seedlings away free
to those who were interested in testing them. Smith
tested and developed new strains of pecans, hickories,
black walnuts, English walnuts, and blight-resistant chestnuts.[55] Of these, probably his work with the chestnut was
most extensive. He began to experiment with the original
stand on his farm and by 1912 he had a large orchard of
American and English chestnuts. In that year, the chestnut
blight struck Virginia. To try to control the blight, the
experiment station at Beltsville, Maryland, made arrangements with Smith to use his orchards as an experimental
center for sprays. The work was unsuccessful; but Smith
continued his interest in the chestnut, and in the 1930's
he discovered a blight-resistant Chinese chestnut and
other strains immune to the disease.[56] Smith also experi-
mented with less-known trees such as the persimmon,
pawpaw, mulberry, and honey locust.[57] He bred the
superior varieties and publicized the great potential of
these trees as food crops. Smith praised the persimmon and
pawpaw for their freedom from pests, hardiness, and
highly nutritive fruit, which animals loved,[58] and the mulberry, an excellent food for pigs, for its rapid growth and
heavy, dependable yield.[59]

Smith's favorite, however, was the honey locust, which
he called the "real sugar tree." [60] In 1923, W. J. Spellman
and Assistant Secretary of Agriculture, Willet Hays, encouraged Smith to work with this promising tree.[61] Smith

[55]Smith, *Tree Crops* (1929), pp. 126–227.
[56]J. Russell Smith, "What's New in Tree Crops?" Northern Nut
Growers Association, *Report of Twenty-Sixth Annual Meeting* (Rockport, Indiana, September, 1955), pp. 78–80.
[57]Smith, *Tree Crops* (1929), pp. 22–107.
[58]Smith, *Tree Crops* (1929), pp. 94–107.
[59]*Ibid.*, pp. 84–85.
[60]Smith, *Tree Crops* (1953), pp. 95–97.
[61]*Ibid.*, pp. 377–78.

constantly praised and exhibited its wonders: It was native and extremely hardy; it was exceedingly prolific; it was highly nutritive as animal fodder and as a possible food for man; and its sugar content of more than a third made it equal to the best sugar beets and better than the yield of the richest crops of sugar cane.[62] Smith's long years of devoted work with the tree made him the recognized expert on the honey locust in America.[63]

Once the best trees were discovered and bred, Smith took measures to demonstrate that tree-crop farming was economically sound. By applying plant genetics, farmers could breed trees that produced a good crop for market. Smith maintained that, contrary to popular opinion, tree crops needed little or no plow cultivation and therefore were a great saving in labor and machinery. From his own successful experience and from that of others, he suggested that the trees be cultivated by mulching, by the application of chemical fertilizers such as nitrate of soda, and by making water pockets to catch rainfall and thus increase the water supply.[64] He never plowed his own highly productive orchards.

Another advantage for the farmer was the two-story agriculture. This consisted of developing fields that combined crop trees and pasture where animals harvested

[62]*Ibid.*, pp. 65–80.

[63]Letter to Professor Smith from Dr. C. C. Newman, Professor of Horticulture at the South Carolina Experiment Station attached to the Clemson Agricultural College, Clemson, South Carolina, September 16, 1928.

[64]J. Russell Smith, "Growing Nuts Without Cultivation," Northern Nut Growers Association, *Report of Nineteenth Annual Meeting* (Toronto, Canada, September, 1928), pp. 52–61. See also Smith, "Soil Erosion and Its Remedy by Terracing and Tree Planting," *Science*, XXXIX(June 12, 1914), 858–861. For the ideas of water pockets and terracing, Professor Smith gave credit to Colonel Freeman Thorpe and J. C. Meyer as examples of creative farmers.

their own fodder from the crop trees and a ground crop.[65] According to Smith, many landowners could keep on with their present crops, using the same land and equipment, and at the same time add a tree crop with small additional cost. Income from this source would be in the nature of clear profit.[66] In addition to the extra income through this permanent agriculture, the farmer would be saving his hill land from the ravages of erosion wrought by the plow and such ruinous but popular crops as corn.

Smith's Writings in Conservation

Again, Smith's writings were the major factor in publicizing his ideas. Smith wrote extensively in many popular magazines,[67] especially from 1905 to 1917, about his own experiments and those of others. His articles not only dealt with tree-crop agriculture but also with plant genetics, soil erosion, irrigation, two-story agriculture and general scientific farming[68] Written in his folksy, personal style, the articles were popular; so much so that for a time, Smith actually considered going into free-lance writing as a career.[69] Frequently his articles brought comments and queries from many interested readers.

Tree Crops, first published in 1929, was his greatest

[65]J. Russell Smith, "Forage Nuts and the Chestnut and Walnut in Europe," Northern Nut Growers Association, *Report of Fourth Annual Meeting* (Washington, D. C., November, 1913), pp. 20–25.

[66]Smith, "Nut Tree Crops as Part of Permanent Agriculture Without Plowing," pp. 104–05.

[67]Among the magazines were: *Forum, Saturday Evening Post, Everybody's Magazine, Country Gentleman, Youth's Companion, Harper's, Survey Graphic, Century, Science, Atlantic, Review of Reviews,* and *Journal of Heredity.*

[68]Examples are: "Plows and Poverty," *Saturday Evening Post,* XLII (July 10, 1909), 14–15, 27–28; "Making Plants and Fruits to Order," *Everybody's Magazine,* XXV (September, 1911), 373–74.

[69]Interview with Professor Smith, July 14, 1953.

single writing in the field. In large part, it summarized
Smith's own work and the work of others experimenting
in tree-crop agriculture. The book was divided into three
parts. Part One gave the philosophy; Part Two dealt with
the various trees. Such chapter headings as "A Stock-Food
Tree—The Honey Locust" and "A Corn Tree—The Chestnut" were suggestive of Smith's aim and approach. Details
were given as to where and how these trees and myriad
others could best be grown. Part Three dealt with "Economics, Farm Applications and National Applications."

One of the most important plans that Smith suggested
in *Tree Crops* to extend the use use of crop trees was the
establishment of "Institutes of Mountain Agriculture." [70]
These institutes were to be variable in size. Some could
be a few acres run by a creative farmer, such as Smith's
friend, John Hershey. Others could consist of thousands
of acres maintained by private business or by philan-
thropic government agencies. Smith's dream was for large,
endowed foundations to continue and elaborate on the
experimental work being done by himself and others.

Smith realized that his book would have a limited
appeal and never approach the circulation of his texts. He
realized, too, that it was difficult to bring changes in established practices of agriculture in a short period of time;
in a letter to a friend he said:

I wrote it expecting practically no financial results and no
actual results in my own lifetime. . . . I expected good results
to follow from firing the imagination of persons like yourself
who would carry the torch on to others as you apparently
are doing.[71]

[70]Smith, *Tree Crops* (1929), pp. 8–20.
[71]Letter from Professor Smith to R. E. Hodgson, Superintendent of
the Southeast Experiment Station of the United States Department of
Agriculture, associated with the University of Minnesota, Waseca,
Minnesota, January 18, 1952.

His pessimism was justified to some extent, because tree crops still do not receive the recognition they deserve and erosion and land waste continue at an alarming rate. However, Smith's ideas continue to be heard by more farmers, soil conservationists, and others interested in the land than he thought possible. Smith considered *Tree Crops* his most important book[72] because of its urgent message that America must "plan or perish." Many must be in accord with him. The book received excellent reviews and is now a classic among agricultural and conservationist literature.[73] As H. L. Crane of the Beltsville Station said,

I think that probably Dr. Smith's greatest contribution has been made in his writings, particularly in his book entitled "Tree Crops." . . . This book has been widely distributed and widely read and he has quite a number following his conversation ideas at the present time.[74]

G. F. Gravatt of the same station wrote that *Tree Crops* was Smith's

. . . monumental work. . . . I have travelled in southern Europe working on the chestnut blight and other tree problems and so I have seen quite a lot of this country ruined by soil erosion which he discusses in different parts of the book; also the good examples of tree crops.[75]

[72]Interview with Professor Smith, July 17, 1953.

[73]The following reviews are important examples: *New York Times Book Review* (February 10, 1929), 5; *Wisconsin Library Bulletin*, XXV (March, 1929), 98; *Geographical Review*, XIX (July, 1929), 528; Raphael Zon, *American Economic Review*, XIX (June, 1929), 272.

[74]Letter to the writer from H. L. Crane, November 10, 1955.

[75]Letter to the writer from G. F. Gravatt, Senior Plant Pathologist, Section of Fruit and Nut Crops, Horticultural Research Service, United States Department of Agriculture, Beltsville, Maryland, November 23, 1955.

Dr. Hodgson of the Waseca Station said in a letter to Smith:

You will never be able to measure the good you have done. I hope that you get a deep satisfaction from having done something worthwhile. Every tree that is planted because of your influence will be better than a hunk of cold stone in your memory.[76]

In 1953, the revised edition of *Tree Crops* was published. In large part it retained the general approach of the original. New statistics, methods of breeding, and accounts of progress made with old and recently developed trees were important additions. So, too, was Smith's section on the people doing creative work in tree-crop experimentation. Part of his purpose in writing the revision was to criticize the laxity of governmental activity in recent years, which aborted the promise of the thirties.[77] It is a commentary on Smith's great energy and devotion to the field, that, at his advanced age, he undertook the tremendous task that such a revision entailed.

Smith's Influence on the Soil Conservation Service

Although Smith did not agree with much of the economic policy of the New Deal, he was gratified that the Roosevelt Administration saw the necessity for conservation measures, and he worked closely with several government services. In fact, it is said that Roosevelt asked

[76]Letter to Professor Smith from R. E. Hodgson, January 8, 1952.

[77]Letter from Professor Smith to William C. Deming, M. D., one of the founders of the Northern Nut Growers Association, October 3, 1951. See also the chapter in the 1953 edition entitled "Who is Working Now?" pp. 361–88.

Smith to be Secretary of Agriculture in his first administration.[78]

The late Dr. Hugh Bennett, the founder of the Soil Conservation Service, unreservedly praised Smith's work and gave him credit for much valuable assistance. He believed that *"Tree Crops* has made an outstanding contribution to conservation throughout this country and, to some extent, in others I have visited." [79] He advised a "thorough reading of the book to see what the good Doctor did to help us with the huge job of conservation." [80] Bennett said the following about the influence of Smith's work at Sunny Ridge:

In the early work of the Soil Conservation Service, a number of us visited Dr. Smith's farm in order to get his views and to study his hillside farming operations for the purpose of carrying this helpful information to other areas of similar character. This was highly valuable in our Hill Culture Program. . . .

Above all, as Bennett further stated:

Our conservation specialists developed the habit of seeking Dr. Smith's advice on soil and water conservation whenever they came to consider what to do with Land Classes 6 and 7 (which represents land too steep for cultivation but in some instances not too steep for fruit culture or nut culture or for the planting of trees that produced excellent livestock).[81]

Smith's Influence on the Tennessee Valley Authority

"This is wonderful. I think you are doing a marvelous

[78]Interviews with Professors Klimm and Willits, who believed that the above was true. Smith made no mention of the subject to the writer.

[79]Letter to the writer from Dr. Hugh Bennett, October 7, 1958.
[80]*Ibid.*
[81]*Ibid.*

piece of work here." [82] These were the words of President
Roosevelt when he visited the Tree Crop Nursery of the
Division of Forestry of the Tennessee Valley Authority in
November, 1934. Arthur E. Morgan, Chairman of the
Board of the T.V.A., having read *Tree Crops*, became interested in the possibilities of an experimental tree-crop
nursery for the Authority. Smith recommended Hershey,[83]
his close friend of long standing, with whom he had ex-
changed many ideas in tree-crop experimentation since
their first meeting in the Northern Nut Growers Association. Smith considered Hershey one of the outstanding men
in the field and looked upon his nut-tree nurseries at Down-
ingtown, Pennsylvania, as models for tree-crop farming.
Hershey worked closely with Smith while he was conduct-
ing the program for the T.V.A., applied many of Smith's
ideas in soil conservation and horticulture and laid the
foundation of a large breeding program. Many of the
trees that he planted, such as strains of blight-resistant
chestnut and varieties of honey locust, were taken from
Smith's farm.[84] Smith was very disappointed and highly
critical of the government for permitting the demise of the
program when Hershey left in 1937.[85]

The Harmon Prize and the Mississippi Floods

As another phase of his interest in conservation, Smith
was concerned with improving methods to alleviate the
disastrous floods on the Mississippi River. He wrote an

[82]John W. Hershey. *Tree Crops and Their Part in the Tennessee Valley* (Knoxville, Tennessee: Division of Forestry, Tennessee Valley Authority, undated).
[83]Smith, *Tree Crops* (1953), p. 378.
[84]Interview with Professor Smith, July 17, 1953.
[85]Smith, *Tree Crops* (1953), pp. 371–81.

article for *Survey Graphic* in July, 1927, entitled "Plan
or Perish," in which he offered a workable plan for the
control of the great river at high water.[86] He criticized
the Army engineers for building only levees instead of
developing adequate spillways for surplus water. He
suggested the need for the construction of reservoirs
which would hold back water and provide a new source
of electric power. He agreed with others about the need
for reforestation as an aid in preventing floods. Furthermore, he asked for the creation of a nonpolitical board
of experts to supervise improved plans for the prevention
of floods.[87] The article was widely reprinted and won him
the Harmon Prize of $500, given by the Harmon Founda-
tion each year to the author of the article that it considered outstanding in stimulating constructive public
opinion in social or industrial fields.

Smith's interest in floods was not confined to the Mississippi. In later years, he drew attention to the similar
problems of the Rio Grande Valley in New Mexico and
Texas, resulting from the silting of the Rio Grande River.
He said it was "one of the most perfect examples of
regional suicide to be found anywhere in the world." [88] He
urged that a private foundation make a complete study
of water, starting with the fall of rain and following
through with surface flow, absorption of water, soil cover,
and land use and all the problems of siltation, channel
filling, and flooding. Ideas similar to those voiced by
Smith were carried out during Roosevelt's Administration.

[86]J. Russell Smith, "Plan or Perish," *Survey Graphic,* (July, 1927),
p. 26.
[87]Smith, "Plan or Perish," *Survey Graphic,* pp. 24–25.
[88]J. Russell Smith, "Plan or Perish," *Soil Conservation,* XIV (October,
1949), 71.

Friends of the Land

Smith and others interested in conservation founded a society called Friends of the Land dedicated to practicing and publicizing the saving of the land by sound measures of soil and water conservation. Among the well-known founders were the late Louis Bromfield[89] and Russell Lord.[90] The title of the society's original publication was *The Land*. Since 1955 is has been called *Land and Water*. Smith has frequently contributed articles to both and has been an honorary member of the society since its foundation. Russell Lord said of Smith, "He is way up there in my estimation, among the true heroes of husbandry in our times and a founder and prime mover in Friends of the Land from 1940 onward." [91] Smith's revised edition of *Tree Crops* in 1953 was sponsored by Friends of the Land.

Continuing Involvement

Despite the problem of age, a factor which has limited his field experimentation and attendance at meetings, Smith is still deeply interested in conservation and in new ways of developing the earth's resources. This is pointed up by his more recent interests such as the development of processes that make large-scale desalting of sea water economically feasible.[92] Although Smith the

[89]This noted author's farm has long been a demonstration center for conservation practices and experimental farming. For many years it has also been the center of research activities conducted by Friends of the Land.

[90]Russell Lord was a former editor of *The Land* and long active in Friends of the Land.

[91]Letter to the author from Russell Lord, November 21, 1955.

[92]Interview with Professor Smith, July 14, 1953. Smith, among others, looked to this experimentation as offering great promise in reclaiming dry lands which for centuries have impoverished many countries, e. g., Israel is a leader in successful pioneering with the desalting process.

geographer is better known than Smith the conservationist
and horticulturist, his work in these fields is perhaps his
most creative and personally satisfying.

VIII

An Overview of Smith's Contributions to Geography and Applied Fields

IN 1956, THE AMERICAN GEOGRAPHICAL SOCIETY AWARDED
the Cullum Geographical Medal to J. Russell Smith, for
his outstanding work in human-economic, regional, and
educational geography, conservation, and college course
development. Smith is the only living geographer to have
this award, the highest honor that can be paid to one in
his profession. The Cullum Medal was a unanimous recognition, by those in the field, of Smith's varied contributions
spanning a period of more than half a century.[1]

SMITH, THE MAN

In some respects, Smith resembles the fast-vanishing
American of an earlier era. In other ways, he has consistently been in the forefront of the modern age and the

[1]Speech of Dr. Lester E. Klimm in the capacity of a Councillor of
the American Geographical Society, delivered on the presentation of the
Cullum Geographical Medal to Professor Smith, November 14, 1956.

evolving world scene.

Smith grew up in "Horatio Alger" times when it was part of the American dream that an obscure farm boy could rise and carve an "empire" in his chosen field. The second half of the nineteenth century was a period of genesis for many aspects of American life. It marked the beginning of new industries, new philosophies, and new educational advances. Smith was one of the multitude of ambitious boys desirous of making a place for themselves in the fast-moving American scene at the turn of the century.

As part of that energetic, hardy, practical, rural stock, imbued with love of the land, he was schooled in the simple American virtues which formed the foundation of the country. To this day, despite the cosmopolitan circles in which he has moved and the distinctions he has merited, Smith retains a high degree of the early American spirit and the elements of the Quaker tradition.

Smith was largely self-made, and to an extent, self-taught. Though he earned degrees in history and economics, he was relatively untrained in his chosen fields of geography, conservation, plant genetics, and writing. His knowledge of these areas was gained to a large extent through direct experience, voracious reading, continuous practice, association with others, and the promptings of his own keen mind and wide-ranging interests. Smith's development was also facilitated by his natural ability to write and his bent towards experimentation. He has always been quick to sense a good idea, whether his own or others, and to apply it towards a practical end. With his versatility, energy, and adaptability, it is quite possible that Smith could have been a success in any field.

Besides being within the mainstream of the American tradition, Smith is solidly enmeshed in the problems and ideas of the twentieth century. He has long been a geographic possibilist, envisioning the great changes that could be wrought by man through the use of scientific invention towards positive ends. Almost from the beginning, too, he has advocated international cooperation and world brotherhood in political, cultural, and economic spheres, often contrary to the frequently nationalistic and isolationist overtones of American domestic and foreign policy.

Besides his realization of the necessity for cooperative action, Smith has always exhibited a strong belief in individualism and self-reliance. This trait was evident in most of his writings, especially those published during the Depression years. In these he struck out against supergovernmental authority, warning against the danger, in time of crisis, of substituting individual initiative and enterprise for increasing dependence upon the state. He did not discount the necessity of long-range governmental planning for the general good, but he consistently believed that an enlightened, responsible public must always hold the reins of power. In this respect, he probed one of the major dilemmas of the twentieth century, the superstate, and perhaps offered the fundamental alternative to totalitarian government—a dynamic, enlightened citizenery.

Concomitant with his belief in an active, informed public was his long advocacy of the idea that education and positive living must incorporate the concept of continuous growth and development. He has constantly lived this precept himself. Through the years his life has been characterized by phenomenal energy and a dynamic unfolding of new powers and interests. Although beyond ninety he is still producing and finding fresh stimulation from new problems, in keeping with his personality and intellectual orientation in terms of the pragmatic and the

positive. Like his spirit, his writing has a buoyancy that
is refreshing. At all times, he was the practical realist who
saw the dilemma of the twentieth century with its haunt-
ing spectres of world chaos and human destruction. Yet,
he believed that men and nations had the potential for
wisdom, for personal and national self-discipline, and for
ethical conduct and that these qualities could be brought
to fruition through education and determined, organized
effort on the part of individuals and governments.

Perhaps disillusioned intellectuals may scoff at Smith's
beliefs as saccharine, nineteenth-century romanticism.
However, in many ways, his was a more reasoned and
balanced approach to the contemporary world than the
nihilism of the existentialists of all descriptions who are
now in vogue. Smith has lived many years and in that
time has experienced many personal and world tragedies.
He has not lost his hope. In the long run, confidence in
the future together with realistic and unselfish world
planning may be the basic factors that will save man from
self-destruction.

SMITH'S CONTRIBUTIONS TO HUMAN-ECONOMIC AND REGIONAL GEOGRAPHY

Aside from his texts, Smith is best known for his work
in human-economic geography. He began his career at an
opportune time, the beginning of the twentieth century,
when geography like many other fields was undergoing
revolutionary changes. From a heavily physical emphasis,
momentum was gathering for the humanization of the
science. Smith's academic preparation placed him in the
mainstream of the new philosophical orientation. With a
background in history and economics he was equipped

with the tools of the social scientist and imbued with an appreciation of the human element.

Smith's choice of the Wharton School of the University of Pennsylvania was also fortunate. The intellectual climate of the Wharton School was geared to a dynamic study of man's needs and activities in relation to the earth, and it was here that college work in human-economic geography was initiated. After only two years, Smith took over full direction of economic geography from Emory R. Johnson and J. Paul Goode. Thus, from the beginning of his career, he was in the fortunate position of having the freedom and opportunity to experiment, to explore, to write, and to grow under his own direction. It was a challenging time when precedents were to be made rather than to be followed.

Smith was far from being alone in propelling the movement towards human geography. Virtually every American geographer had been affected by William Morris Davis' tradition-breaking announcement that geography was the study of the relationship between earth and man. Geography had suddenly come alive; it pulsed with the life of human activities and offered practical help to man in his struggle with the earth. This new concept of geography was in sharp contrast to the previous esoteric study of landforms or the mechanical listing of products and locational facts.

Initially, because of his meager background, Smith had to rely on the thoughts and writings of those better versed in the field. Accordingly, he was influenced by the many American and European geographers who were attempting to give meaning, organization, and content to human geography.[2] Smith's human-economic approach was,

²*Supra*, Chap. II, pp. 20–23.

therefore a synthesis drawn in part from the ideas of the leading theorists of the time. But it developed into a pattern that was distinctly his own.

Smith's articles and especially his advanced texts, such as *Industrial and Commercial Geography* and *North America,* contributed to systematizing and expanding economic-geography writing beyond the previously narrow statistical and commercial orientation. Using basic organizing principles, particularly that of human use, he was among the first to stress meanings, causes, and relationships rather than unrelated facts and figures. A deeper insight into the nature and functioning of economic activities that result from man's dynamic relationship to his environment was thus made possible. The early incorporation into his writings of such new fields as climatology, conservation, plant genetics, industrial management, and scientific invention was unique at the time and helped broaden the content base of geography.

Smith was also a pioneer among American geographers in applying a regional, human-geographic treatment to a major work. In *North America* his analysis of the countries of the northern hemisphere on the basis of human-use regions helped unite the human and the physical in a regional treatment that approached a truer geographic synthesis. This work filled a great need in American geographic literature because here, for the first time, a regionalization of the continent was presented in terms of the way human beings use it, rather than on the customary basis for physiographic divisions.

It is interesting to see the developing educational and philosophical tone of Smith's writings. In many respects he was decades ahead in his thinking. His books and articles, especially those written from the 1920's on, invariably attempted to instill basic attitudinal values. His broadening vision reflected his growth from a narrow, nationalistic, somewhat deterministic view, to an emphasis on world brotherhood, economic internationalism, long-range cooperative planning, and geographic possibilism.

As he matured, he came to see that the role of modern man, aided by technology and the academic disciplines, must be one of fostering international prosperity and world citizenship. For example, from the early decades of the century he pointed out that underdeveloped areas must be helped to realize their potential, rather than be exploited as the pawns of colonial empires. He emphasized again and again that a high degree of moral responsibility, trained, intelligent leadership, and active, creative citizenship, in all peoples, was necessary for survival as free individuals in the modern world. These themes were fundamental in the bulk of his writings and echoed the view that the ultimate aim of geography, and indeed of all learning, is essentially a moral and philosophical one. In this respect, his works have been consistently in the mainstream of those contributing to the new thinking in the social studies and allied fields.

Some critics may assert that Smith cannot be credited with organizing new geographic theory and that, working with the environmental relationship concept, he reached his height in the theoretical aspect of the field in the mid-1920's. In a strict sense, this may be true. Smith did not have the training for the statistical and land-survey techniques that began in the 1930's and culminated in the modern definition of geography as the study of areal differentiation. Furthermore, after the mid-1920's his interest was divided among educational geography, conservation, and the application of geography to specialized agriculture.

However, taking a narrow view, pure originality, in a specific sense, cannot be attributed even to such pioneers as Davis, Herbertson, Semple, Ratzel, Ritter, or to any one of the European or American geographers working in the new field of human geography.[3] No man labors alone. He is part of his times and carries within himself the past of his civilization. Who can be given exclusive credit for any "new" theory, idea, or insight? Interpretation is an evolutionary process. The trend towards the humanization of science can be traced back to such a varied chain of influences as the humanism of the Renaissance, the Enlightenment of the seventeenth and eighteenth centuries, the romanticism of the nineteenth, and the rapid industrialization of the twentieth.

When it comes to a consideration of the degree and nature of Smith's contribution, an evaluation of his work is easier to attempt. He certainly did not make as purely an original contribution to human-geographic theory as the geographers mentioned above, many of whom preceded him. However, he was among the first of the American geographers to recognize the value and potential of the new field of human geography. Though not a pure researcher, he did important creative work, through his writings and course development, in helping to organize, clarify, and apply the new theories to economic geography. His work helped broaden the content, meaning, and practical application of economic geography to all phases of man's activity, and facilitated the transition of American geography from a purely physical orientation to one combining attention to both human and physical elements.

Theories in themselves are not enough. They must be

[3]*Supra*, Chap. II, pp. 20–34.

tested, modified, and given practical extension so that people can see and feel their value. This is one of Smith's own dictums. Therefore, it is a moot question whether the theory or its working operation is more important. In reality, it is of greater meaning to consider both elements as essential parts of an harmonious whole.

SMITH'S CONTRIBUTIONS TO GEOGRAPHIC EDUCATION

From the early 1920's on, Smith's energies were devoted largely to the writing of elementary texts and it is for this work that he is probably best known. After witnessing the destruction and insanity of World War I, he became increasingly convinced of the necessity of educating people to work together with mutual understanding and respect. He believed he could be of greatest service by writing texts that might be influential in instilling these attitudes in American youth.

As late as the 1920's geography at the elementary level was a rather dreary, narrow subject, with little long-run educational value. As with *Industrial and Commercial Geography* at the college level, Smith's *Human Geography, Book One, Peoples and Places,* and his *Human Geography, Book Two, Regions and Trade,* helped launch a kind of revolution in elementary school geography.

Again, Smith was not the originator of human geography at the elementary level. Many others[4] had long been attempting to make grade-school geography texts more than unscientific wonder books of exotic facts, or dry, locational and statistical accounts of the physical earth. They had achieved varying degrees of success. Smith, however, with true artistry and creativity, most

[4]*Supra,* Chap. IV, pp. 112–20.

successfully combined a meaningful, scientifically sound,
human approach with the basic principles of child psychology. The resulting texts were realistically geared to
the child's intellectual and emotional level. His geographic stories were so alive with interest and color that
children could identify themselves with the characters
and vicariously join in their activities. People and their
everyday activities in all parts of the world, rather than
merely rocks and volcanoes and meaningless lists of
products, were the core of Smith's approach and the crux
of his success.

Along with his translation of geographic facts and
ideas into language that could be understood and enjoyed
by children, Smith was the first to incorporate fully into
his texts the evolving long-range attitudinal objectives
of human geography. Smith realized that attitudinal learning must begin early to be effective. In his elementary
texts he attempted to imbue children with a feeling of
oneness with people of other lands. Other basic attitudes
his texts constantly fostered were an appreciation of the
earth and the need for conserving its resources, intelligent
and active citizenship, critical judgment, and creative
activity. All of these goals seem commonplace today, but
in the early twenties they were a unique addition to elementary texts.

In addition to philosophical innovations, Smith's books
early reflected other elements of the modern text. His
many captioned illustrations carried out the human theme
and formed an integral part of each book. He graded material developmentally. He provided interesting, varied
exercises, activities, and vocabulary lists. There was a wide
selection of maps, some of them specially developed for
the texts, such as the human-use maps of the 1930's. Comprehensive teacher's manuals accompanying the texts gave

philosophical background and practical suggestions for teaching geography meaningfully according to the new methods. Thus, beginning with his human geographies of the early 1920's, Smith's texts were a crystallization on the elementary level of the new geographic theories and, as such, were among the first to be written within the scope of the modern philosophy of social studies.

In all, Smith produced three geography series covering grades three through seven. Various texts have gone through numerous editions and, in all, his books have sold millions of copies. From the beginning to the present, they have been leaders in their field.

Developments in textbook writing influence curriculum changes. Since Smith's books were pace setters, they probably played a significant part in the curriculum modifications that took place in the elementary school during the twenties and thirties. This may be especially true with respect to the introduction of a more human approach and the orientation of social studies teaching in terms of long-range, meaningful knowledges, skills, and attitudes.

The great volume of their sales brought his texts to a wider audience than any of his other works. They also made him a wealthy man. Thus Smith probably was prompted to write them for practical as well as for educational purposes. Yet, whether one consideration outweighed the other is not of fundamental importance. What is significant, in the long run, is the part these texts may have played and continue to play in developing children into more reasoning and creative human beings.

SMITH'S CONTRIBUTIONS TO COLLEGE COURSE DEVELOPMENT

Smith also made important contributions to the development of college courses in geography. In fact, it can be said without reservation that the Department of Geography and Industry in the Wharton School of Business of the University of Pennsylvania and the Department of Economic Geography of Columbia University's Graduate School of Business were really his creations.

The work at Wharton was precedent setting because this institution offered the first courses that could be called human-economic geography. Although he built on the foundation laid by Johnson and Goode, Smith deserves the credit for developing economic geography at Wharton into a recognized and mature discipline with departmental status. For the first time such basic new concepts as a human orientation, the significance of climatic factors, regional analysis, regional planning, and the relation of geographic factors to industrial management were fully incorporated into course work in geography. At Wharton, Smith trained students and teachers who became well known in education, business, and government; his work there served as a guide to other institutions. In 1957, the University of Pennsylvania awarded Smith the honorary degree of Doctor in Economic Science.

From 1919 to 1944, the date of his retirement, Smith did similarly important creative work on both the undergraduate and graduate levels, in instituting and developing a Department of Economic Geography at Columbia's School of Business. His interest and that of his colleagues influenced the establishment of the Doctor of Philosophy degree to be given under the auspices of the School of Business, later the Graduate School of Business. Smith and his colleagues developed graduate seminars noted for their emphasis upon thought, creativity, and thorough, systematic research. The right to grant the Doctor of

Philosophy degree brought increased prestige to economic geography as well as to professional business training at Columbia. In 1929, Columbia awarded to Smith an honorary Doctor of Science degree in recognition of his contributions.

Thus, Smith's work in course development on both the undergraduate and graduate levels was significant. In America the momentum for the humanization of geography was begun on the college level in the schools of business. Smith was one of the important educators to help launch.this revolution.

SMITH'S CONTRIBUTION IN APPLIED GEOGRAPHY

Smith has always been interested in such contemporary problems as the development of the world's food resources, the trade relations of nations, and the economic policies of the Depression period. Without question, however, Smith's most important contribution to applied geography was in the related fields of conservation and plant genetics. Here he did some of his most original and, in many respects, most creative work. It was also work undertaken largely without compensation—a real labor of love.

Smith's feeling for the land as a living entity stemmed partly from his rural inheritance and early life on the farm; so, too, did his long awareness of the urgent need to preserve nature's resources. From the beginning of the century the theme of conservation has been a constant one with Smith, permeating all his writings, from his technical articles and books in the field to his geography texts on all levels.

Smith not only helped awaken interest in the need for

conservation; he also perfected methods to save and develop the land. Of these, his attention to crop-bearing trees was most significant. At Sunny Ridge, his experimental farm, he bred numerous varieties of different kinds of trees and devised improved means of grafting and cultivation. Many of the new strains had a higher rate of productivity and a great resistance to blight. These crop-bearing trees not only provide food for man and beast but also help preserve the erosion-prone hill lands from washing away nature's precious work of centuries. Again, Smith disseminated his ideas in conservation through articles and books, such as his classic *Tree Crops*.

In addition to his experimentation and writing, he is also a respected member of such conservation organizations as the Northern Nut Growers Association and Friends of the Land, which he helped found. His advice and aid have been sought frequently by these groups as well as by the Soil Conservation Service, the Tennessee Valley Authority, and various governmental agricultural stations. It can be readily said that his work has given him a respected place among those in conservation and plant genetics.

SUMMARY

J. Russell Smith is thus a unique man, of unusual energy and versatility. His restless, probing, creative mind caused him to go beyond the narrow subject bounds of a single academic discipline and to view knowledge as a related whole. Some may criticize Smith for his occasional inaccuracies, his untested theories, or, at times, his de-emphasis of specific details. These criticisms are sometimes justified and when detrimental to truth and objectivity reflect definite weaknesses which, as a professional geographer, Smith should have eliminated. On the other hand, it must be remembered that Smith's goal was different from that of the pure research specialist. To him an idea had worth only if it were put to work. We must see Smith the academic geographer, the generalist, as well as the synthesizer and experimenter, as many others have seen Shaler, Smith's "unseen master," as more concerned with awakening minds than with imparting specific information.

Essentially, he has the talent of a great teacher and pragmatist because of his ability to grasp significant ideas from the mass of theoretical research and to organize and develop them in applied writings, comprehensible to the layman. This ability is also an important form of genius and creativity. Because of it, his work has frequently had a greater chance of reaching and influencing the public than the specialized studies of many pure researchers who, though more strictly original, present findings in a highly stylized, technical language beyond the grasp of the ordinary man.

A final insight into Smith's many-faceted nature may be gained from remarks of Richard Hartshorne who once said:

May I add that in character he is a delightful person who has maintained, up to the last time I saw him, the essential spirit of youth, respecting others in terms of what they could contribute regardless of age, so that one never felt the weight of his age or position in talking to him.[5]

[5]Letter to the author from Richard Hartshorne, Professor of Geography, University of Wisconsin, November 14, 1955.

Appendix

The Development of Modern
Geography in Europe and America

To see J. Russell Smith's role in the mainstream of geographic development, it is necessary to trace briefly the evolution of the subject, especially from the nineteenth century when the foundations of modern geography were laid.

EUROPEAN BEGINNINGS

European geography has had a long and distinguished history. Many of the developments in America had their roots in the experience of the Old World.

The Preclassical Period of
The Eighteenth Century

The majority of the geographers of the early preclassical period did not consider geography to be a separate science; rather they were concerned with its practical utility in other fields, such as history and cartography. Essentially, they limited its study to a description of the physical phenomena of the earth.[1]

In the latter part of the eighteenth century, however, such men as Phillippe Buache,[2] Johann Christoph Gatterer,[3] and Immanuel Kant[4] broke away from this approach and prepared the way for the scientific treatment of geography. This new orientation stemmed from their use of natural regions and their growing attention to the relationship of physical factors to plant, animal, and human life.

The Classical Period

The synthesis of the ideas of the preclassicists into scientific terms was largely the work of Alexander von Humboldt and Karl Ritter. Modern geography can really be said to have begun with their work.[5] Humboldt demonstrated the principles of causality and coordination in geographic method through the comparative study of similar phenomena in various parts of the earth's surface. Ritter established the concept of regional treatment and the importance of the human factor.[6]

Humboldt (1769–1859) was mainly a physical geog-

[1]Richard Hartshorne, *The Nature of Geography*, Prepared for the Association of American Geographers (Lancaster, Pa.: The Science Press Printing Company, 4th printing, 1951), pp. 40–41.

[2]Buache of France developed the theory of the continuous network of mountain systems as the basis for regional divisions.

[3]Gatterer of Germany continued Buache's work and made it the basis for a physical division of the world. His work influenced contemporaries and later, Humboldt.

[4]Kant's consideration of physical features in terms of their ultimate importance to man is the key to the new spirit of geography as developed by the preclassical school.

[5]Hartshorne, *The Nature of Geography*, pp. 48–49.

[6]Robert E. Dickinson and O. J. R. Howarth, *The Making of Geography* (Oxford: The Clarendon Press, 1933), p. 248.

rapher who, through his extensive field work,[7] acquired a large store of factual information on which a system of geography could be founded. His method was scientific and aided in breaking the teleological hold on geographic thought. His description of the physical world in his greatest work *Cosmos* was, at the time, the most exact and comprehensive compendium of modern science and the most complete history of its development ever attempted.

Specifically, Humboldt's chief contributions to geography were his investigations of horizontal temperature distribution and its representation by isotherms, the vertical decrease of temperature in different latitudes, the correlation of plant distribution with physical conditions, the distribution of terrestrial magnetism, and most important, the systematic geographic studies of separate regions.[8]

Ritter (1779–1859), with his wide background in history, aimed at analyzing history in terms of the physical environment. Ritter vigorously opposed what he considered the trend in "pure" geography to overemphasize the *natürliche Landschaft*. He insisted that geography must describe and explain all the present conditions of an area. Ultimately, the efficacy of his work was hindered by his overemphasis of the human aspect at the expense of the environment, and his failure to establish a satisfactory causal relationship between the two.

Fundamentally, there were two major differences between Humboldt and Ritter. Ritter studied regions of such large size that he seldom completed a full study of all

[7]Humboldt made field studies in Central and South America, Russia, and Siberia.

[8]Griffiths Taylor, *Geography in the Twentieth Century* (New York: The Philosophical Library, 1953), pp. 5, 50–59, 131–32.

related phenomena; Humboldt described in great detail the areas he visited, some quite small, and so was able to provide a relatively complete picture. Ritter wished to study all the related phenomena of a region together; Humboldt, as a practical scientist, limited his work to an intensive and systematic study of one or two sets of phenomena in a region, such as the relation of altitude to plant life.

The Post-Classical Period

The "classical period" ended with the deaths of Humboldt and Ritter in 1859. During the following decade, academic geography was dominated by the school founded by Ritter, and was characterized by a shift from systematic regional geography to regional geography concerned primarily with man in relation to his natural environment.

The new focus on the interaction of man and nature was fostered by the theory of evolution, first preached by Kant and brought to fruition by Darwin and others, which placed increasing emphasis upon the environment and environmental change. As a result, the development of geography in the second half of the nineteenth century witnessed the advent of the genetic interpretation of landforms, the birth of the science of geomorphology, and the study of the distribution and activities of man as largely determined by environmental conditions. For the most part, human and physical geography did not develop as one; rather, a dualism developed during the second half of the nineteenth century which caused different geographers to pursue one aspect of geography to the exclusion of the other.

Physical geography. Oscar Peschel (1826–75), professor of geography at Leipzig, played a significant part in laying the foundations of modern physical geography. He helped further the scientific spirit in geography and led geographers to study primarily the morphology of landforms as well as the influence of landforms on human history.

Ferdinand von Richthofen, the next important figure after Peschel, was a professor at Bonn, Leipzig, and Berlin. Although his extensive field trips led him to examine the relation of surface features to man's activities, his greatest contribution was to physical geography. He is generally considered the founder of geomorphology.[9]

Human geography. The other line of geographic development, the human aspect, was pursued by Friedrich Ratzel in Germany and Paul Vidal de la Blache and Jean Brunhes in France. The formulation of a more specifically human geography may be dated from the publication of Ratzel's *Anthropogeographie* in 1882. Ratzel's work was a product of the great advances made in scientific knowledge. However, he misconstrued the scientific meaning of evolution and made human adaptation to the environment through natural selection the keynote of his method. Therefore, despite its title, *Anthropogeographie* was highly deterministic and gave man a static role in relation to an all powerful nature.[10] In other words, man's activi-

[9]Walter Crane, *Modern Geographers* (New York: J. Wiley and Sons, Inc., 1921), p. 35.

[10]Although there is no literal English translation of Ratzel's work, Ellen Churchill Semple expounded Ratzel's views in such of her works as *Influences of Geographic Environment on the Basis of Ratzel's System of Anthropogeography* (New York: Henry Holt & Co., 1911); *American History and Its Geographic Conditions* (Boston: Houghton, Mifflin & Co., 1913); *The Geography of the Mediterranean Region; Its Relation to Ancient History* (New York: Henry Holt & Company, 1931).

ties, developments, and aspirations were almost completely conditioned by his environment.[11] Little or no credit was given to human will and initiative.

Ratzel's rigid determinism, though acclaimed by some, met with severe criticism from other human geographers. Outstanding among those opposed to his theories were Vidal de la Blache and Brunhes, whose work brought about a remarkable development of human geography in France. These geographers helped develop the school of "possibilism."

Vidal de la Blache, the founder of the modern French school of geography, and specifically of modern regional geography, saw the necessity for detailed, synthetic studies in geography. His writings, and those of Brunhes and others whom he inspired, helped discredit the principle of determinism. His main aim in geography was to study cause and effect in related phenomena, and then to coordinate and establish general principles through the comparative study of different parts of the globe, along lines suggested by Humboldt and Ritter. On the basis of his studies and observations, he concluded that man's mode of life was the result not only of the physical environment, but also of a complex of factors: social, historical, and psychological. The environment contained a number of possibilities, but their utilization was dependent entirely upon human selection.[12]

Brunhes, Vidal de la Blache's most brilliant disciple, was appointed in 1907 to the first chair of human geography in either Europe or the United States, that at Lausanne. Later, the College de France in Paris created a similar post for him, which he held from 1912 until his

[11]Semple, *Influences of Geographic Environment,* pp. 1–8.
[12]Paul Vidal de la Blache, *Principles of Human Geography* (New York: Henry Holt and Co., 1926), p. 321.

death in 1929. Brunhes further defined the field of human geography and took as his basis the evidence of man's use and occupancy of the environment. Into this study, he introduced a principle of classification and a method of treatment covering not only the basic necessities of food, clothing, and shelter, but also social, political, and economic activities. True to Vidal de la Blache's principles, Brunhes advocated and practiced the regional method with strong emphasis on man's dynamic interaction with his environment.[13] This detailed regional treatment was further developed by Herbertson in England and Hettner in Germany during the first decades of the twentieth century.

DEVELOPMENTS IN THE UNITED STATES

In a sense, America was a century behind Europe in geographic theory. While on the continent geography developed a human, regional orientation, nineteenth century America was primarily concerned with the physical aspects of the subject. The greatest names in the field were geologists such as G. K. Gilbert, Major John W. Powell, Louis Agassiz, Nathaniel Southgate Shaler, Rollin D. Salisbury, and William Morris Davis. Publications of geographers at the end of the nineteenth century consisted largely of morphological discussions.

The physical emphasis in the United States can be somewhat explained by the fact that our history had long been and was still largely one of wilderness conquest. The very diversity of the American landscape made the land appear to be a self-sufficient field of study, especially

[13]Jean Brunhes, *Human Geography* (Chicago: Rand, McNally & Co., 1920), pp. 24–27, 454–56, 514–17.

to the later physiographers, who first gave the subject
scientific standing.[14]

Early Progress

Initially, recognition came to geography in the United
States as an instrument of measurement in subdividing
the public domain.[15] Great interest developed in geographical and topographical surveys, usually conducted
by the Department of War or of the Interior as new terri-
tories were explored. Several of these surveys were of
outstanding importance in the development of geographic
thought. Such studies were the joint surveys of the American and Mexican boundary in 1854–56, the survey of
possible railroad routes to the Pacific in 1853–55, and
especially the geographic and geological work of F. V.
Hayden, Captain George M. Wheeler, and Major Powell.

Until 1867, geology was a handmaiden to geography in
expeditions whose main object was topographical recon-
naisance. In later years, the geologists were placed in
charge of independent field research. Geologists came into
such dominance in the United States Geological Survey,
which superseded the earlier surveys, that geographical
work, for a time, was all but eliminated. Major Powell,
among others, recognized, however, that sound geological
research was based on geographic factors.

The End of the Nineteenth Century

Activity during the period from 1880 to 1900, though

[14]Isaiah Bowman, *Geography in Relation to the Social Sciences* (New
York: Charles Scribner's Sons, 1934), pp. 220–22.
[15]Under the Ordinance of May 20, 1785, the officer in charge of the
public or national domain was called the Geographer of the United
States.

still mainly of a physical nature, showed a widening of geographic considerations. The regional surveys of the federal and state governments, the publications of such groups as the National Geographic Society and the American Geographical Society, and the work done in universities, all indicated the new trend. Although interest in exploration was still important, mappings and surveys were increasingly conducted on the basis of explanatory studies of the physical features of selected regions. Analysis of the genesis of landforms and of regional climatic conditions was coming into prominence.

The analytical work of the period was exemplified by the regional studies that appeared in the first volume of the monographs published by the National Geographic Society in 1895.[16] Among these were Bailey Willis' "The Northern Appalachians" and William Morris Davis' "The Physical Geography of Southern New England." A foreshadowing of the coming interest in broad regional delimitation and the technique of classification was afforded by Major Powell's "Physiographic Regions of the United States" in the same issue. Of the state surveys, those by Rollin D. Salisbury, "The Physical Geography of New Jersey," and by Ralph Tarr, "The Physical Geography of New York State," were most significant.

Despite the predominant interest in physical geography, such leaders as Nathaniel Southgate Shaler[17] retained an appreciation of a broader approach to geography, especially by the inclusion of the human factor. Although his courses were always labeled geology, much of his work

---

[16]*National Geographic Monographs*, I–X (New York: American Book Company, 1895). Prepared under the auspices of the National Geographic Society.

[17]Shaler, one of the founders of American geography, was Professor of Geology at Harvard from 1864 to 1906. He was also the teacher of William Morris Davis.

was geographic in focus. Many consider him the fore-runner of modern human geography in the United States.[18] Justification for this conclusion can be found in his pioneer works, *Nature and Man in America* and *Man and the Earth*.[19]

Progress in the Twentieth Century

The turn of the century found several important cur-rents of geographic thought under way, which led to developments of great significance in geographic science. The year 1903 was outstanding in the history of American geography. In that year occurred the initial move in the founding of the Association of American Geographers, the increased clarification of geographic theory, the cre-ation of the first department of geography in an American university, the publication of two notable books in the field of anthropogeography, the appearance of the first article of major dimensions in economic geography, and important contributions in political and historical geog-raphy.

The first two events can be attributed largely to William Morris Davis, who was the leader in formulating and projecting geographic theory in America at the turn of the century.[20] Although fundamentally a dynamic geologist and the founder of physiography, he had a strong appreciation for geography. His articles from

[18]H. Phillip Bacon, "Fireworks in the Classroom, Nathaniel South-gate Shaler as a Teacher," *Journal of Geography*, LIV (October, 1955), 349.

[19]Nathaniel Southgate Shaler, *Nature and Man in America* (New York: Charles Scribner's Sons, 1891); *Man and the Earth* (New York: Fox, Duffield and Company, 1905).

[20]Charles C. Colby, "Changing Currents of Geographic Thought in America," *Annals of the Association of American Geographers*, XXVI (March, 1936), 16-18.

1900–03 helped to define the subject as, in essence, the relationship between the earth and the organisms that live upon it. In 1904, he founded the Association of American Geographers.

Geography in the universities. From 1900 onward the universities played an ever-increasing role in the evolution of geographic thought. In addition to the scholarly work of Shaler and Davis at Harvard, there was that of Albert Perry Brigham at Colgate, Richard Elwood Dodge at Teachers College, Columbia University, J. Russell Smith at Wharton, and Charles Redway Dryer at Indiana.

At California, physiography had gained the status of a separate department. In 1903, Cornell University announced a summer school of geology and geography with a staff that included Ralph Stockman Tarr, Albert Perry Brigham, Charles McMurry, and Ray H. Whitbeck.

The high point was reached in 1902–03 when the University of Chicago created a separate Department of Geography under the leadership of Professors Thomas C. Chamberlin and Rollin D. Salisbury, both formerly of the Department of Geology. Their aim was to occupy the ground intermediate between geology and climatology, on the one hand, and history, sociology, political economy, and biology, on the other. J. Paul Goode's appointment in 1903 introduced work in economic geography which he brought from the Wharton School of the University of Pennsylvania. Periodically, Ellen Churchill Semple offered courses in anthropogeography. From the beginning, too, emphasis was placed on the regional approach. The department at Chicago received immediate recognition, and its demonstration of the importance of geography, at the university level, helped stimulate interest in the discipline.

Human geography. The turn of the twentieth century found a growing interest in the human aspects of geography, demonstrated in the publications of the geographical societies and in the work of such pioneers as Shaler, Cyrus C. Adams, Brigham, Henry Gannett, Semple, and, later, Smith.

The year 1903 was again important because of the publication of *American History and Its Geographic Conditions*[21] by Semple and *Geographic Influences in American History*[22] by Brigham. These epoch-making books brought anthropogeography firmly to the attention of American geographers and won considerable public interest. With modifications, the trend toward human geography continued, until today it is an intimate part of the subject.

Economic geography. A good deal of the trend toward human geography was stimulated by work in its commercial and economic phases. In 1903, Smith published an article entitled "The Economic Geography of the Argentine Republic." In this study, Smith set a high standard for the aspect of the science which it heralded.[23] However, the great awakening in the field came ten years later with the publication of his *Industrial and Commercial Geography*.[24]

The first World War gave research opportunities and practical experience to a score or more of economic geog-

[21]Ellen Churchill Semple, *American History and Its Geographic Conditions* (Boston: Houghton, Mifflin & Co., 1913).

[22]Albert Perry Brigham, *Geographic Influences in American History* (Boston: Ginn & Company, 1903).

[23]Colby, "Changing Currents of Geographic Thought in America," p. 10.

[24]J. Russell Smith, *Industrial and Commercial Geography* (New York: Henry Holt and Company, 1913).

raphers who served on various government boards.[25] Following the war, the number of workers in the field increased rapidly. In 1924, Clark University launched *Economic Geography*, a journal that created a new literature and stimulated new thought and types of research. Since the early decades of the century, economic geography has progressed rapidly and is now an important and established branch of the field.

Political geography. Another fruit of the inclusion of the human element was the growth of modern political geography, which developed far beyond the earlier attention to chiefly locational facts. A stride was made in 1903 with the publication of I. C. Russell's "Geography and International Boundaries," [26] one of the first geographic studies in this field.

World War I provided the greatest opportunities up to that time for workers in political geography. A group of geographers, with headquarters at the American Geographical Society, served on the commission that prepared for American participation in the peace negotiations. Later, they were advisers at the Peace Conference in Paris. These experiences provided invaluable material and stimulated thought and analysis along many lines. Following the war, Isaiah Bowman, the executive of the group, gave a succinct statement of the problems and scope of political geography in his *The New World: Problems in Political Geography.*[27] This authoritative volume clarified and sys-

[25]For example, Smith served on the War Trade Board along with Harlan H. Barrows, Ray H. Whitbeck, and Nels A. Bengston.

[26]Israel Cook Russell, "Geography and International Boundaries," *Bulletin of the American Geographical Society,* XXXV (August, 1903), 147–59. See also Colby, "Changing Currents of Geographic Thought in America," p. 24.

[27]Isaiah Bowman, *The New World: Problems in Political Geography* (Yonkers-on-Hudson, New York: World Book Company, 1921).

tematized materials and concepts and thereby provided a basis for further research in the field. In recent years, research in political geography in this country has tended to the investigation of carefully defined problems employing modern methods and techniques. An example is Richard Hartshorne's "Geographic and Political Boundaries in Upper Silesia." [28] The events of the past decades have led to the development of this field as an important area of study.

Historical geography. Historical geography entered university circles in the summer of 1904, when Harlan H. Barrows introduced his famous course entitled "Influences of Geography on American History." This and similar courses aided in bringing a more analytical approach to history and in showing the intimate relationship between history and geography.

Barrows' first work was highly deterministic, in keeping with the influence of Ratzel and Semple when anthropogeography was new in America. Later, he greatly modified his point of view to a more reasoned and realistic balance between man and nature, translated in terms of "human ecology." [29]

Geographic theory. Geography in America, as in Europe, has been burdened by a duality in theory and method between its human and physical aspects.[30] This duality evolved as a phase of the history of natural science

[28]Colby, "Changing Currents of Geographic Thought in America," p. 29.

[29]Harlan H. Barrows, "Geography as Human Ecology," *Annals of the Association of American Geographers,* XIII (March, 1923), 3. In keeping with his new approach, Barrows in 1921 changed the name of his original course in historical geography to "Historical Geography of the United States."

[30]Preston E. James and Clarence F. Jones (eds.), *American Geography: Inventory & Prospect* (Syracuse: Syracuse University Press, 1954), p. 28.

and came as an inheritance from the period when geography was buried under the weight of nineteenth-century geology and later obscured by overemphasis on physiography and climatology. Thus, for two generations before 1900, physical geography eclipsed human geography on both sides of the Atlantic and clouded geographic theory and method for at least a decade after 1900.[31] Today there is general agreement that geography deals with earth and man and that a regional focus is essential.

Within the field, at present, there are two main centers of interest. The first involves more intensive field work, pure research, and a greater knowledge of physical geography. It calls for intensive study of areal or regional units of varying dimensions and the recognition, mapping, classification, interpretation, and comparison of unit areas. The second is social in character and grows out of an active interest in human activities and problems, as, for example, the wise utilization of land and other natural resources.[32] However, the two aspects are complementary. The explanatory description of unit areas inevitably leads to a consideration of land use. Conversely, many problems of land utilization cannot be understood or solved unless studied against their physical setting.

Applied geography. With the expansion of geographical content into both human and physical elements, immense growth has taken place in what is termed applied fields of geography. Such phases of geography as those dealing with plant and animal life, agriculture, conservation, military affairs, medicine, population distribution, and cultural

[31]Almon E. Parkins, "The Geography of American Geographers," *Journal of Geography,* XXXIII (July, 1934), 222.
[32]James and Jones (eds.), *American Geography: Inventory & Prospect,* pp. 14–17, 29–31.

patterns are just a few of the specialized areas that have developed since the beginning of the century. The future promises an increase rather than a diminution of this trend as the utility of geography in exploring and understanding related human and natural phenomena is more fully appreciated.[33]

Geography joins the social sciences. Paralleling the growth of the human aspect of geography has come its increasing inclusion within the realm of the social sciences.[34] Today, the influence of geographic factors on human activities is recognized. The varied earth with its infinitude of problems will ever be a part of man. Accordingly, many institutions of learning have assigned geography to the social science department.

The intimate affiliation of human geography with the social sciences has turned attention to ethical elements within geography's content and purpose. One of the major aims of human geography is to improve society by increasing man's control over his environment for positive ends. Ideally, this spirit leads to an ever-widening deployment of geography from the local community to the entire world in seeking to fulfill both ethical and material objectives.

---

[33]*Ibid.*, pp. 70–553.
[34]Bowman, *Geography in Relation to the Social Sciences*, p. 223.

Bibliography

J. RUSSELL SMITH'S PUBLICATIONS

Elementary Geography Texts and Supplements (All were published by the John C. Winston Company, Philadelphia).

Human Geography, Book One: Peoples and Countries, 1921, 1926, 1931, 1935, 1938, 1939.

Human Geography, Book Two: Regions and Trade, 1921, 1926, 1930, 1931, 1932.

Home Folks: A Geography for Beginners, 1927, 1930, 1934, 1939.

Our Neighboring Continents, 1930.

Our State and North America, 1930.

World Folks, 1930, 1931, 1936, 1938, 1939, 1945.

American Lands and Peoples, 1932, 1935, 1938, 1939, 1942, 1946.

Home Folks in Texas, 1932.

Foreign Lands and Peoples, 1933, 1936, 1938, 1939, 1942, 1943, 1945.

Human Use Geography, Book One, 1934, 1936, 1938, 1939, 1942.

Human Use Geography, Book Two, 1934, 1936, 1938, 1939, 1940, 1943.

Other World Neighbors The British Empire, Africa, Asia, Latin America, 1934, 1936, 1939, 1942.

Our Country and Northern Neighbors, 1934, 1936, 1939, 1942, 1946.

Our European Neighbors, Homelands and Outlying Areas, 1934, 1936, 1939, 1942, 1946.

Our Industrial World, 1934, 1935, 1936, 1938, 1939, 1942 1948.

Our Industrial World with *Pennsylvania Supplement,* 1936, 1939, 1948.

New Jersey, People, Resources and Industries of the Garden State, 1935.

California—Life, Resources and Industries of the Golden State, 1936.

Human Use Geography, Book Two with *Kansas Supplement,* 1936.

Human Use Geography with *Virginia Supplement,* 1936.

New York, The Empire State, 1942.

Geography and World War Two, 1943, 1944.

Geography of the Americas for Elementary Schools, 1946.

Geography of Europe, Asia, Africa for Elementary Schools, 1946.

*Neighbors Around the World, 1947, 1952, 1959.

*Our Neighbors at Home, 1947, 1954.

*Neighbors in the Americas, 1948, 1954, 1957.

*Neighbors Across the Seas, 1950, 1954, 1956.

*Neighbors in the United States and Canada, 1951, 1954, 1957.

College Texts

Industrial and Commercial Geography. New York: Henry Holt and Company, 1913, 1925.

Smith, and Phillips, M. Ogden. *Industrial and Commercial Geography.* New York: Henry Holt and Company, 1946.

Smith, Phillips, M. Ogden, and Smith, Thomas Russell. *In-*

*The above elementary texts were written by Smith in collaboration with Frank E. Sorenson.

dustrial and Commercial Geography. New York: Henry Holt
and Company, 1955.

North America. New York: Harcourt, Brace and Company,
1925.

Smith, and Phillips, M. Ogden, *North America.* 2d ed. rev.
New York: Harcourt Brace and Company, 1940. 3d ed. rev.
1942.

Other Books

The Organization of Ocean Commerce. Philadelphia: The
University of Pennsylvania, 1905.

The Ocean Carrier. New York: G. P. Putnam's Sons, 1908.

The Story of Iron and Steel. New York: D. Appleton and
Company, 1908.

The Elements of Industrial Management. Philadelphia: J. B.
Lippincott Company, 1915.

Commerce and Industry. New York: Henry Holt and Company, 1916.

The Influence of the Great War on Shipping. Washington,
D.C.: Carnegie Endowment for International Peace, 1918.

The Influence of the Great War on Shipping. New York:
Oxford University Press, 1919.

The World's Food Resources. New York: Henry Holt and
Company, 1919.

Tree Crops. New York: Harcourt, Brace and Company, 1929.

Smith *et al. Methods of Achieving Economic Justice.* Purcellville, Va.: Blue Ridge Herald Press, 1935.

Men and Resources. New York: Harcourt, Brace and Company, 1937.

The Devil of the Machine Age. New York: Harcourt, Brace
and Company, 1941.

Tree Crops. 2d ed. rev. New York: The Devin-Adair Company, 1953.

Booklets

Our Faith and the Causes of War. Philadelphia: W. H. Jenkins, Printer, 1920.

The Proper Organization of Geography in American Education. Philadelphia: The John C. Winston Company, 1922.

Geography and the Higher Citizenship. Philadelphia: The John C. Winston Company, 1925.

School Geography and the Regional Idea. Philadelphia: The John C. Winston Company, 1925.

Geography and Our Need of It. Chicago: American Library Association, 1928.

World-Picture Building: Globe-Map Studies in Creative Geography. New York: Paul Garrigue, 1930.

Articles

Conservation, Natural Resources, and Horticulture
"American Forestry: A New Career," *Forum,* XXXIII (May, 1902, 356–62.

"Plows and Poverty," *Saturday Evening Post,* XLII (July 10, 1909), 14–15, 27–28.

"Breeding and Use of Tree Crops," *American Breeders Magazine,* I (Second Quarter, 1910), 86–91.

"Making Plants and Fruits to Order," *Everybody's Magazine,* XXV (September, 1911), 373–74.

"Does Your Farming Fit Your Land?" *Country Gentleman,* LXXVII (March 30, 1912), 2–3, 18.

"Fortunes From Fertility," *Country Gentleman,* LXXVII (April 27, 1912), 2–3, 29–30.

"How Rural Delivery Brings Good Roads," *Country Gentleman,* LXXVII (June 15, 1912), 3, 26.

"A Master Farmer and His Dozen Farms," *Country Gentleman,* LXXVII (July 20, 1912), 4–5, 20.

"A Missionary of Better Farming," *Country Gentleman*, LXXVI (August 17, 1912), 2–3, 25–26.

"The Chances for Eastern Apple Growers," *Country Gentleman*, LXXVI (September 17, 1912), 4–5, 16.

"The Menace of the Chestnut Blight," *Outing*, LXI (October 1912), 76–83.

"The Subduing of the Little Sand Farms," *Country Gentleman*, LXXVII (November 17, 1912), 2–3, 17.

"Tonics for Sandy Soils," *Country Gentleman*, LXXVII (November 23, 1912), 4–5, 22.

"Fortunes From Fertilizers," *Country Gentleman*, LXXVII (November 30, 1912), 4, 23.

"Nut Growing and Tree Breeding and Their Relation to Conservation," Northern Nut Growers Association, *Report of Third Annual Meeting* Lancaster, Pa., 1912, 59–64.

"Agriculture of the Future," *Harper's Monthly Magazine*, CXXVI (January, 1913), 273–81.

"The Little Worlds of the Chesapeake," *Country Gentleman*, LXXVIII (January 11, 1913), 6–7, 30–31.

"A Land of Berry Farms," *Country Gentleman*, LXXVIII (February 1, 1913), 10–11.

"Breaking Precedents in Delaware," *Country Gentleman*, LXXVIII (March 29, 1913), 8–9, 28.

"The Farm Missionary's Gospel," *Country Gentleman*, LXXVII (April 5, 1913), 3–4, 42.

"The Land That Found Itself," *Country Gentleman*, LXXVIII (May 31, 1913), 14–15.

"The Conservative Viewpoint," *Country Gentleman*, LXXVIII (June 7, 1913), 12.

"The Doctor's New Job," *Country Gentleman*, LXXVIII (June 28, 1913), 6–7.

"The Rabbit and the Greyhounds," *Everybody's Magazine*, XXIX (July, 1913), 76–86.

"Nut Farming For Tomorrow," *Country Gentleman*, LXXVIII (July 5, 1913), 23.

"Men Who Wail and Men Who Win," *Country Gentleman*, LXXVIII (July 12, 1913), 4–5.

"Cooperation Without Cost," *Country Gentleman*, LXXVIII (August 2, 1913), 1–2.

"More Than a One Man Job," *Country Gentleman*, LXXVIII (August 2, 1913), 12.

"Big Profits From Little Pets," *Country Gentleman*, LXXVIII (August 16, 1913), 8–9.

"Five Hundred Year Old Pastures," *Country Gentleman*, LXXVIII (September 27, 1913), 7–8.

"Forage Nuts and the Chestnut and Walnut in Europe," Northern Nut Growers Association, *Report of Fourth Annual Meeting*, Concord, New Hampshire, (November, 1913), 20–25.

"The Making of Successful Farmers," *Youth's Companion*, LXXXVII (November, 1913), 442–43.

"Nut Trees That Bear Dollars," *Country Gentleman*, LXXVIII, (November 8, 1913), 10–11.

"Pecans and the Patient Waiter," *Country Gentleman*, LXXVIII (December 6, 1913), 10–11.

"Pigs, Peas, and Pecans," *Country Gentleman*, LXXVIII (December 27, 1913), 4–5.

"Selling Nut Trees. The Nomenclature of Northern Pecans," Northern Nut Growers Association, *Report on Fifth Annual Meeting*, Evansville, Indiana, 1914, 54–61.

"Milk for the Babies," *Country Gentleman*, LXXIX (January 3, 1914), 10–11.

"Meat—the Sugar Planter's Hope," *Country Gentleman*, LXXIX (January 10, 1914), 44–45.

"Apples Without Plowing," *Country Gentelman*, LXXIX (April 18, 1914), 6–7, 27.

"The Real Dry-Farmer," *Harper's Monthly Magazine*, CXXVIII (May, 1914), 836–47.

"Brain That Beats Brawn," *Country Gentleman*, LXXIX (May 2, 1914), 5–6.

"When Do You Cut Your Clover Hay?" *Country Gentleman*, LXXIX (May 9, 1914), 8.

"Soil Erosion and Its Remedy by Terracing and Tree Planting," *Science*, XXXIX (June 12, 1914), 858–62.

"Two-Story Farming," *Century*, LXXXVIII (July, 1914), 383–88.

"Agriculture of the Garden of Eden," *Atlantic Monthly*, CXIV (August, 1914), 256–62.

"Avocations That Counted," *Harper's Weekly*, LIX (September 12, 1914), 262.

"Nut Tree Crops and a New Agriculture," Northern Nut Growers Association, *Report of Sixth Annual Meeting*, Rochester, New York, 1915, 30–36.

"Neglected Northern Pecans," *Country Gentleman*, LXXX (January 9, 1915), 7–8, 40.

"A Cure for Drought," *Country Gentleman*, LXXX (January 23, 1915), 8.

"Manna in the Mountains," *Country Gentleman*, LXXX (January 30, 1915), 3–4.

"The Doctor's Good Road," *Country Gentleman*, LXXX (February 27, 1915), 3–4.

"Trees That Eat Hay," *Country Gentleman*, LXXX (June 5, 1915), 8, 26.

"The 'Ben Davis' Hen," *Country Gentleman*, LXXX (July 17, 1915), 24–25.

"Gardens of Eden," *Country Gentleman*, LXXX (August, 1915), 3–4.

"Stopping Runaway Waters," *Country Gentleman*, LXXX (September 25, 1915), 9–10.

"Riehl Fun With Nuts," *Country Gentleman*, LXXX (October 9, 1915), 3.

"Feeding the Neighbors," *Country Gentleman*, LXXX October 30, 1915), 3–4.

"Dismissing the Professor," *Survey Graphic*, XXXV (November 6, 1915), 131–34.

"Better Roads for Less Money," *Country Gentleman*, LXXX (November 13, 1915), 3–4.

"A Georgia Tree Farmer," *Country Gentleman*, LXXX (December 4, 1915), 5–6.

"The Oak Trees and Man's Environment," *Geographical Review*, I (January, 1916), 3–19.

"Shade Trees That Bear Nuts," *Country Gentleman*, LXXXI (January 8, 1916), 4.

"Grafting Walnuts and Hickories," *Country Gentleman*, LXXXI (January 29, 1916), 3–4.

"The Persian Walnut, A Typical Problem in Tree Breeding," *Journal of Heredity*, VII (February, 1916), 55–60.

"Farming Appalachia," *Review of Reviews*, LIII (March, 1916), 329–36.

"Where to Market Your Apples," *Country Gentleman*, LXXXI (April 29, 1916), 3–4.

"The Dry Farmers of Rome," *Century*, XCII (May, 1916), 75–82.

"English Walnuts in the East," *Country Gentleman*, LXXXI (June 17, 1916), 8–9.

"The New Farmer and His New Water-Supply," *Century*, XCIII (December, 1916), 273–79.

"Tree Crops for Dry Lands," *Journal of Geography*, XV (December, 1916), 105–12.

"Food-producing Trees," *American Forestry*, XXIII (April, 1917), 228–33.

"Shall the World Starve?" *Country Gentleman*, LXXXII (June 9, 1917), 3–4, 24.

"Next Year's Food," *Century*, XCIV (August, 1917), 633.

"Quit Fooling and Talk Sense," *Country Gentleman*, LXXXII (August 4, 1917), 4–5, 28.

"Food or Famine?" *Century* XCIV (September, 1917), 685–89.

"The Scientific City and Its Food Supply," *Journal of Geography*, XVIII (April, 1919), 121–28.

"Nut Tree Crops as a Part of Permanent Agriculture Without Plowing," Northern Nut Growers Association, *Report of Fifteenth Annual Meeting*, New York City, 1924, pp. 103–7.

"The Reindeer Industry in America," *Scottish Geographical Magazine*, XL (March, 1924), 74–88.

"Some Observations With Reference to Nut Trees in Distant Lands," Northern Nut Growers Association, *Report of Seventeenth Annual Meeting*, Lancaster, Pa., 1926, pp. 72–77.

"Nut Trees Suitable for the Chesapeake Country," Northern Nut Growers Association, *Report of Eighteenth Annual Meeting*, Easton, Md., 1927, pp. 70–75.

"Plan or Perish," *Survey Graphic*, LVIII (July 1, 1927), 370–77.

Smith and W. C. Lowdermilk. "Wealth From Mississippi Mud," *World Review*, V (November 14, 1927), 129.

"Growing Nuts Without Cultivation," Northern Nut Growers Association, *Report of Nineteenth Annual Meeting*, Toronto, Canada, 1928, pp. 52–61.

"The Second Year of Drought," *New Republic*, LXVI (April 1, 1931), 169–70.

"End of An Epoch," *Survey Graphic*, LXVI (July 1, 1931), 333–36.

"Double-Topworking Hickory Trees," Northern Nut Growers Association, *Report of Twenty-Third Annual Meeting* (Washington, D. C. (September, 1932), pp. 115–17.

"Drought: Act of God and Freedom," *Survey Graphic*, XXIII (September, 1934), 412–14.

"What's New in Tree Crops?" Northern Nut Growers Association, *Report of Twenty-Sixth Annual Meeting*, Rockport, Indiana, 1935, pp. 78–80.

"Sound Use of Land and Water," *Survey Graphic*, XXIV (February, 1935), 63–67.

"Tree Crops, A Permanent Agriculture," Northern Nut Growers Association, *Report of Twenty-Eighth Annual Meeting*, College Park, Md., 1939), pp. 67–70.

"The Chestnut in Farm Economy," Northern Nut Growers Association, *Report of Thirty-First Annual Meeting*, Roanoke Va., 1940, pp. 33–35.

"Flash in the Pan?" *The Land*, I (Winter Issue, 1941), 27.

"Notes from the Blue Ridge," Northern Nut Growers Association, *Report of Thirty-Third Annual Meeting*, Toronto, Canada, 1942, pp. 49–50.

"Tree Crops, An Unappreciated Possibility," *Bio-Dynamics*, III (Summer, 1943), 38–40.

"Tree Crops for Feed, Food, Soil Conservation and the Northern Nut Growers Association," Northern Nut Growers Association, *Report of Fortieth Annual Meeting*, Beltsville, Md., 1949, pp. 43–49.

"Regional Suicide," *The Land*, VIII (Autumn, 1949), 314–18.

"Plan or Perish," *Soil Conservation*, XIV (October, 1949), 71.

"Soil Destruction or Tree Crops in the Tropical Forests," *Journal of Geography*, XLVIII (October, 1949), 303–5.

"Pecans in Northern Virginia," Northern Nut Growers Association, *Report of Forty-Second Annual Meeting*, Guelph, Ontario, 1951, pp. 45–47.

"Grass Silage and the Future," *The Land*, XII (Winter, 1953-54), 441–43.

Economic and Commercial Geography

"The Philippine Islands and American Capital," *Popular Science Monthly*, LX (June, 1899), 186–92.

"Western South America and Its Relations to American Trade," *Annals of the American Academy of Political and Social Science*, XVIII November, 1901), 446–68.

"The Economic Geography of the Argentine Republic," *Bulletin of the American Geographical Society*, XXXV (February, 1903), 130–43.

"The Economic Geography of Chile," *Bulletin of the American Geographical Society*, XXXVI (January, 1904), 1–15.

"The British System of Commercial Administration," *Annals of the American Academy of Political and Social Science*, XXIV (November, 1904), 507–25.

"The Economic Importance of the Plateaux in Tropic America," *Bulletin of the American Geographical Society*, XXXVII (August, 1905), 461–68.

"Ocean Freight Rates," *Political Science Quarterly*, XXI (June, 1906), 237–63.

"Ocean Freight Rates and Their Control by Line Carriers," *Journal of Political Economy*, XIV (November, 1906), 525–41.

"Harbor Facilities of London," *Annals of the American Academy of Political and Social Science*, XXIX (March, 1907), 386–89.

"The Intercontinental Railroad," *North American Review,* CLXXXV (June 7, 1907), 283–92.

"The Cost and Profits of Steel-Making in the United States," *Quarterly Journal of Economics,* XXII (February, 1908), 261–73.

"The Development of Commercial Centers," *Bulletin of the American Geographical Society,* XLII (May, 1910), 346–55.

"The World Entrepôt," *Journal of Political Economy,* XVIII (November, 1910), 697–713.

"The Panama Canal and Its Influence on Ocean Rates and Traffic," *Railway Gazette,* (July 12, 1912), 6–7.

"The World Carriers and the Panama Canal," *Journal of Geography,* XI (March, 1913), 227–31.

"Foreword" on "The American Industrial Opportunity," *Annals of the American Academy of Political and Social Science,* LIX (May, 1915), vii–xii.

"The Reconstructed City," *Annals of the American Academy of Political and Social Science,* LIX (May, 1915), 283–89.

"The Small Corporation—A Pitfall," *Engineering Magazine,* XLIX (August, 1915), 672–78.

"The Island and the Continent at War," *Century,* XCI (March, 1916), 742–47.

"Neutralized World," *Review of Reviews,* LVI (August, 1917), 170–71.

"Economic Access and Neutralization of Waterways," *Proceedings of the Academy of Political Science,* VII (July, 1917), 272–78.

"The Selective Draft in Industry," *Century,* XCIV (September, 1917), 137–42.

"Price Control Through Industrial Organization," *Annals of the American Academy of Political and Social Science,* LXXIV (November, 1917), 280–87.

"Some Economic Aspects of the American Food Supply," *Proceedings of the American Philosophical Society,* LVII (1918), 501–12.

"The American Trade Balance and Probable Trade Tendencies," *Annals of the American Academy of Political and Social Science,* LXXXIII (May, 1919), 86–118.

"Trade and a League of Nations or Economic Internationalism," *Annals of the American Academy of Political and Social Science,* LXXXIII (May, 1919), 287–306.

"The Great Valley, A Function of Limestone," *Journal of Geography,* XX (May, 1921), 161–75.

"Geography and Geographers," *Literary Review,* III (April 7, 1923), 584.

"Long-Range Planning for the Regularization of Industry," *New Republic,* LXIX (January 13, 1932), 1–25.

"The Idiocy of Economic Nationalism in the Light of Climatic Regions and Other Factors Which Differentiate Lands," *Proceedings of the World Federation of Education Associations,* (1933), 235–41.

"Make Jobs or Perish," *Survey Graphic,* XXVI (August, 1937), 430–34.

"Grasslands and Farmlands as Factors in the Cyclical Development of Eurasian History," *Smithsonian Report,* (1944), 357–84.

Education in Geography

"Geography in Germany. I. The Primary and Secondary Schools," *Journal of Geography,* I (November, 1902), 420–30.

"Geography in Germany. II. The University," *Journal of Geography,* I (December, 1902), 448–57.

"Economic Geography and Its Relation to Economic Theory and Higher Education," *Bulletin of the American Geographical Society,* XXXIX (August, 1907), 472–82.

"Geography and the Higher Citizenship," *Progressive Education,* II (June, 1925), 77–80.

"Elements of Geography and the Geographic Unit," *School and Society,* XVII (March, 1927), 41–49.

"The Contribution of Economic Geography to the Preparation of a Teacher of Geography," *Teachers College Record,* XXX (January, 1929), 354–63.

"The Most Civilizing Subject in the Curriculum," *World Review,* VIII (March 11, 1929), 81.

"Geography for School Superintendents," *School Executives,* L (June, 1931), 478–79.

"How Geography Contributes to General Ends in Education," *The Teaching Geography, Thirty-second Yearbook of the National Society for the Study of Education.* Bloomington, Illinois: Public School Publishing Co., 1933. Pp. 29–41.

"The Geography of American Geographers," *Journal of Geography,* XXXIII (September, 1934), 221–30.

"Are We Free To Coin New Terms?" *Annals of the Association of American Geographers,* XXV (March, 1935), 17–22.

"Geographic Education's Contribution to World Citizenship," *Secondary Education,* VIII (March, 1939), 87–91.

"Geography, A Group of People in a Place," *Education,* LX (December, 1939), 195–200.

"What Shall the Geography Teacher Teach in the Elementary School?" *Journal of Geography,* XLVI (March, 1947), 101–8.

"Suggestions for Illustrating Books," *Annals of the Association of American Geographers,* XXXII (September, 1942), 316.

"How to Understand a Nation," *Journal of Geography,* LIII (February, 1954), 71–84.

"Geography and World Citizenship," *Social Education,* XXI (May, 1957), 205–6, 208.

Miscellaneous

"A Community of Clubs," *Country Gentleman,* LXXVIII (August 9, 1913), 14–15.

"Ellsworth Huntington, Geographer," *Bulletin of the Geographical Society of Philadelphia,* XIV (January, 1916), 19–23.

"Why We Hate the Food Speculator," *Country Gentleman,* LXXXII (June 23, 1917), 1–2.

"What We Save When We Cut Out Booze," *North American Review,* CCVI (August 12, 1917), 34.

"Building Ships to Beat the Submarines," *Review of Reviews,* LVI (October, 1917), 393–96.

"Faculty Birth Rate: Should It Be Increased?" *Eugenics,* III (December, 1930), 458.

"Mackinder: 1942," *New Republic*, CVII (September 14, 1942), 322–23.

"For Birth Control," *The Land*, VII (Spring, 1948), 49–51.

Smith and Smith, Henrietta Stewart. "The Third Revolution and World Peace," *The Friend*, CXX (February 24, 1949), 275–77.

MATERIAL FROM SMITH'S FILES AND UNPUBLISHED MEMORANDA

Circulars, Unpublished Articles, and Memoranda

"Contest for Superior Acorns of the White Oak, Chestnut Oak, and Burr Oak." Undated circular issued by Professor Smith.

"Fifty Dollars for the Best Black Walnut in America." Undated circular issued by Professor Smith.

"Honey Locust Beans." Undated circular published at Sunny Ridge Nursery, Swathmore, Pa.

"Memorandum for Members of the Council of the Association of American Geographers for the Year 1941 and for the Year 1942," April 17, 1942.

Memorandum on the "Honey Locust," November 25, 1947.

"Memorandum to Members of the Council of the Association of American Geographers," April 17, 1942.

Memorandum entitled "Notes on Papers, Discussions, and Procedure at the Meeting of the Association of American Geographers at Columbus, Ohio," December, 1946.

"The Neighbors Series." Memorandum dated March 4, 1948.

"Prizes for Best Native Nuts of North America." Undated circular issued by Professor Smith.

"The Seminar, Research, and Geographical Writing." Unpublished paper on the conduct of geographical seminars, delivered at a joint meeting of the Association of American Geographers and the American Society of Professional Geographers (Madison, Wisconsin, December 28, 1948).

"Smith Answers His Critics of the *Tree Crops* Book." Unpublished article dated February 23, 1951.

"The Use of Type Studies in Elementary Geography." Unpublished article, dated October 6, 1928.

"Where are the Best Honey Locust Trees? Cash Prizes for their Discovery." Undated circular issued by Professor Smith from Sunny Ridge Orchards, Round Hill, Virginia.

"Where is the Best Honey Locust Tree?" Undated circular announcing a contest sponsored by Professor Smith from his Sunny Ridge Orchards, Round Hill, Virginia.

Correspondence

Professor Smith's correspondence was extensive and varied in keeping with his many interests. Especially helpful in shedding light on his activities in conservation and plant genetics were his communications with members of the United States Department of Agriculture, the American Genetic Association, the Northern Nut Growers Association, the Division of Forestry of the Tennessee Valley Authority, professors of horticulture and agricultural economics at universities throughout the country, editors of farm newspapers and journals, and individual farmers and researchers.

Significant in revealing personal beliefs and interests were Smith's letters to his sons Thomas and Stewart.

Insight into his work and activities in professional geography was given by his correspondence with such noted fellow geographers, some now deceased, as Nels Bengston, George F. Carter, George B. Cressey, and Carl O. Sauer. Smith's communications with the late Emory R. Johnson shed light on his early activities at the Wharton School of the University of Pennsylvania.

Carbon copies of all of the above correspondence can be found in the author's personal files. The original letters are in Smith's files at his home in Swarthmore, Pennsylvania.

BOOKS AND REPORTS USED IN THE STUDY

Adams, Cyrus C. *An Elementary Commercial Geography.* New York: D. Appleton & Co., 1902.

Bowman, Isaiah. *Forest Physiography.* New York: J. Wiley & Sons, 1911.

—— *Geography in Relation to the Social Sciences.* New York: Charles Scribner's Sons, 1934.

—— *The New World; Problems in Political Geography.* Yonkers-on-Hudson, New York: World Book Company, 1921.

Branom, Mendel E., and Branom, Fred K. *The Teaching of Geography.* Boston: Ginn & Co., 1921.

Brigham, Albert Perry. *Geographic Influences in American History.* Boston: Ginn & Company, 1903.

Brinton, Howard. *Friends for 300 Years.* New York: Harper and Brothers, 1952.

—— *Quaker Education in Theory and Practice.* Pendle Hill, Pa., 1940.

Brunhes, Jean. *Human Geography.* Chicago: Rand, McNally & Co., 1920.

Chisholm, George G. *Handbook of Commercial Geography.* London: Longmans, Green and Co., 1890.

Crane, Walter. *Modern Geographers.* New York: J. Wiley and Sons, Inc., 1921.

Dawson, Edgar. *The Teaching of the Social Studies.* New York: The Macmillan Co., 1928.

Dickinson, Robert E. and O. J. R. Howarth. *The Making of Geography.* Oxford: The Clarendon Press, 1933.

Frye, Alexis. *New Geography, Book One.* Boston: Ginn and Co., 1921.

Griffin, Paul F. "The Contribution of Richard Elwood Dodge to Educational Geography" (Unpublished Ph.D. dissertation, Faculty of Philosophy, Columbia University, 1952).

Hartshorne, Richard. *The Nature of Geography.* Prepared for the Association of American Geographers. Lancaster, Pennsylvania: The Science Printing Press Company, 4th printing, 1951.

Herbertson, Andrew, J. *Man and His Work; An Introduction to Human Geography*. London: A. and C. Black, 1899.

Hershey, John W. *Tree Crops and Their Part in the Tennessee Valley*. Knoxville, Tennessee: Division of Forestry, Tennessee Valley Authority, undated.

Hofstadter, Richard. *Social Darwinism in American Thought*. Boston: The Beacon Press, 1958.

Huntington, Ellsworth T. *The Character of Races*. New York: Charles Scribner's Sons, 1924.

——— *Civilization and Climate*. New Haven: Yale University Press, 1915.

——— *The Pulse of Asia*. Boston: Houghton, Mifflin and Company, 1907.

——— *World Power and Evolution*. New Haven: Yale University Press, 1919.

James, Preston E., and Jones, Clarence F. (eds). *American Geography: Inventory & Prospect*. Syracuse: Syracuse University Press, 1954.

Johnson, Emory R. *Life of a University Professor: An Autobiography*. Philadelphia: The University of Pennsylvania, 1931.

Jones, Llewellyn R. and Bryan, Patrick W. *North America*. London: Methuen & Co., Ltd., 1924.

Jones, Rufus M. *The Quakers in the American Colonies*. London: Macmillan and Co., Limited, 1911.

Klimm, Lester E., Starkey, Otis P. and Hall, Norman F. *Introductory Economic Geography*. New York: Harcourt, Brace and Co., 1937.

National Geographic Monographs, I–X. New York: American Book Company, 1895.

Odegard, Peter. *The American Public Mind*. New York: Columbia University Press, 1925.

"Report of Geography Conference." *Report of the Committee of Ten on Secondary School Studies*. Published for the

National Education Association. New York: American Book Company, 1894.

Report of the Isthmian Canal Commission, 1899–1901. Washington: Government Printing Office, 1904.

Report of Second Annual Meeting, Northern Nut Growers Association, Ithaca, New York, 1911.

Roorbach, Orville A. *Bibliotheca Americana, 1820–1852.* New York: Peter Smith, 1939.

Sauer, Carl O. *The Morphology of Landscape.* University of California Publications in Geography, Vol. II, No. 2. Berkeley, California: University of California Press, 1925.

Semple, Ellen Churchill. *American History and Its Geographic Conditions.* Boston: Houghton, Mifflin & Co., 1913.

—— *Influences of Geographic Environment on the Basis of Ratzel's System of Anthropogeography.* New York: Henry Holt & Co., 1911.

—— *The Geography of the Mediterranean Region; Its Relation to Ancient History.* New York: Henry Holt & Company, 1931.

Shaler, Nathaniel Southgate. *Nature and Man in America.* New York: Charles Scribner's Sons, 1891.

—— *The Story of Our Continent.* Boston: Ginn & Company, 1894.

—— *The United States of America.* New York: D. Appleton & Co., 1894.

Starkey, Otis P. and Christians, William F. *Exploring Our Industrial World.* Philadelphia: The John C. Winston Co., 1938.

Tarr, Ralph S. *Elementary Physical Geography.* New York: Macmillan and Co., 1896.

Taylor Griffiths. *Geography in the Twentieth Century.* New York: The Philosophical Library, 1953.

Tilden, John N. *Commercial Geography for Academies, High Schools, and Business Colleges.* Boston: Leach, Shewell, and Sanborn, 1891.

Tryon, Rolla M. *The Social Studies as School Subjects.* New York: Charles Scribner's Sons, 1935.

Van Metre, Thurman W. *A History of the Graduate School of Business, Columbia University.* New York: Columbia University Press, 1954.

Vidal de la Blache, Paul. *Principles of Human Geography.* New York: Henry Holt and Co., 1926.

Wertenbaker, Thomas Jefferson. *The Golden Age of Colonial Culture.* New York: New York University Press, 1942.

Whitbeck, Ray H. and Finch, V. C. *Economic Geography.* New York: McGraw-Hill Book Company, Inc., 1924.

Woodman, Charles M. *Quakers Find a Way, Their Discoveries in Practical Living.* Indianapolis: Bobbs-Merrill, 1950.

Who's Who in America. Chicago: Marquis-Who's Who, Inc., 1957; 1960.

ANNALS, PROCEEDINGS, AND JOURNALS OF LEARNED SOCIETIES

Bacon, H. Phillip. "Fireworks in the Classroom: Nathaniel Southgate Shaler as a Teacher," *Journal of Geography,* LIV (October, 1955), 349–53.

Barrows, Harlan H. "Geography as Human Ecology," *Annals of the Association of American Geographers,* XIII (March, 1923), 1–13.

Bowman, Isaiah. "Commercial Geography as a Science: Reflections on Some Recent Books," *Geographical Review,* XV (April, 1925), 285–94.

Brigham, Albert Perry. "The Organic Side of Geography, Its Nature and Its Limits," *Bulletin of the American Geographical Society,* XLII (June, 1910), 442–52.

Brigham, Albert Perry and Dodge, Richard E. "Nineteenth Century Textbooks of Geography," *The Teaching of Geography. Thirty-second Yearbook of the National Society for the Study of Education.* Bloomington, Illinois: Public School Publishing Co., 1933. Pp. 3–27.

Brown, Ralph H. "Letter to Rev. Jedidiah Morse, Author of

the *American Universal Geography,*" *Annals of the Association of American Geographers,* XLI (September, 1951), 187–92.

Colby, Charles C. "Changing Currents of Geographic Thought in America," *Annals of the Association of American Geographers,* XXVI (March, 1936), 1–37.

Davis, William Morris. "The Present Trend of Geography," *111th Annual Report of the University of the State of New York* (1898), 192–202.

—— "The Progress of Geography in the United States," *Annals of the Association of American Geographers,* XIV (December, 1924), 159–215.

—— "A Retrospect of Geography," *Annals of the Association of American Geographers,* XXII (December, 1932), 211–30.

—— "Systematic Geography," *Proceedings of the American Philosophical Society,* XL (April 3, 1902), 235–59.

Dodge, Richard Elwood. "Some Problems in Geographic Education with Special Reference to Secondary Schools," *Annals of the Association of American Geographers,* VI (1916), 3–18.

—— "William Morris Davis—An Appreciation," *Journal of Geography,* XXXIII (April, 1934), 148–50.

Dryer, Charles Redway. "A Century of Geographic Education in the United States," *Annals of the Association of American Geographers,* XIV (September, 1924), 117–249.

Fenneman, Nevin M. "The Circumference of Geography," *Annals of the Association of American Geographers,* IX (1919), 3–11.

—— "Physiographic Divisions of the United States," *Annals of the Association of American Geographers,* VI (1916), 19–98.

Goode, J. Paul. "A College Course in Ontography," *Annals of the Association of American Geographers,* I (1911), 111.

Hall, Robert Burnett. "The Geographic Region: A Résumé," *Annals of the Association of American Geographers,* XXV (September, 1935), 122–36.

Herbertson, Andrew J. "The Major Natural Regions: An

Essay in Systematic Geography," *Geographical Journal*, XXV (1905), 300–12.

Horn, Ernest. "Possible Defects in the Present Content of American History as Taught in the Schools," *Sixteenth Yearbook of the National Society for the Study of Education*, 1920. Pp. 156–73.

Huntling, Ella. "Modern Trends in the Teaching of Geography," *Proceedings of the Fifth Biennial Conference of the World Federation of Education Associations*. Dublin, Ireland: World Federation of Education Associations, 1933. Pp. 239–49.

Jefferson, Mark. "Some Considerations on the Geographical Provinces of the United States," *Annals of the Association of American Geographers*, VII (1917), 3–16.

Joerg, Wolfgang L. G. "The Geography of North America: A History of Its Regional Exposition." *Geographical Review*, XXVI (October, 1936), 640–63.

—— "The Subdivision of North America into Natural Regions: A Preliminary Inquiry," *Annals of the Association of American Geographers*, IV (1914), 55–83.

Keasbey, Lindley M. "The Principles of Economic Geography," *Political Science Quarterly*, XVI (September, 1901), 476–85.

—— "The Study of Economic Geography," *Political Science Quarterly*, XVI (March, 1901), 79–95.

"Keeping Pace with the Advancing Curriculum," *Research Bulletin of the National Education Association*, III (September and October, 1925), 150–56.

Kennamer, Lorrin G. "Beginnings in Geographic Education," *Journal of Geography*, LII (February, 1953), 71–84.

Leighly, John. "What Has Happened to Physical Geography?" *Annals of the Association of American Geographers*, XLV (December, 1955), 309–18.

McMurray, Charles A. "A Course of Study in Geography for the Grades of the Common School," *Supplement* to the Fourth Yearbook of the National Herbart Society, IV (1899), 121–73.

Parkins, Almon E. "The Geography of American Geographers," *Journal of Geography*, XXXIII (September, 1934), 221–30.

Roorbach, George G. "The Trend of Modern Geography, A Symposium," *Bulletin of the American Geographical Society*, XLVI (November, 1914), 798–808.

Sauer, Carl O. "The Survey Method in Geography and Its Objectives," *Annals of the Association of American Geographers*, XLV (March, 1924), 17–33.

Semple, Ellen Churchill. "Louisville: A Study in Economic Geography," *Journal of School Geography*, IV (December, 1900), 361–70.

Stockton, Charles H. "The Commercial Geography of the American Interoceanic Canal," *Journal of the American Geographical Society*, XX (June, 1888), 75–93.

Tower, Walter Sheldon. "A Field for Studies in Regional Geography," *Bulletin of the American Geographical Society*, XXXVIII (August, 1906), 481–89.

——— "The Human Side of Systematic Geography," *Bulletin of the American Geographical Society*, XL (September, 1908), 522–30.

——— "Scientific Geography: The Relation of Its Content to Its Subdivisions," *Bulletin of the American Geographical Society*, XLII (ovember, 1913), 801–25.

Von Englen, O. D. "The World's Food Resources," *Geographical Review*, VIII (May, 1919), 170–92.

"War Services of the Members of the Association of American Geographers," *Annals of the Association of American Geographers*, IX (1919), 67.

Whitbeck, Ray H. "Adjustments to Environment in South America: An Interplay of Influences," *Annals of the Association of American Geographers*, XVI (March, 1926), 1–11.

——— "Human Geographer," *Annals of the Association of American Geographers*, XX (June, 1930), 73–81.

——— "The Present Trend of Geography in the United States," *Geographical Journal*, XXXV (April, 1910), 420–25.

——— "Thirty Years of Geography in the United States," *Journal of Geography*, XX (April, 1921), 98–114.

UNIVERSITY CATALOGUES

Wharton School of Finance and Commerce

First Annual Report of the Wharton School of Finance and Economy, University of Pennsylvania, May 1, 1884.

The following catalogues of the University of Pennsylvania were used. All were published in Philadelphia by the University. *Catalogue of the University of Pennsylvania*, 1896–1918.

Graduate School of Business, Columbia University

Columbia University Bulletin of Information, 1919–20, 19th Ser., No. 21. New York: The Arbor Press, Inc., April 14, 1919.

The following catalogues of Columbia University were used. All were published in New York by the University. *Columbia University Bulletin of Information*, 1920–1948.

INTERVIEWS

The author had innterviews with the following: Professor Smith, July 7, 14, 17, and 21, 1953; Mrs. Henrietta Smith, July 7, 1953; Myra Light, secretary to Professor Smith, July 15, 1953 Dr. Herman Otte, Professor of Economic Geography, Graduate School of Business, Columbia University, May 17, 1957; Dr. Lester E. Klimm, Professor of Geography at the Wharton School of Finance and Commerce of the University of Pennsylvania, July 17, 1957; Dr. Alfred H. Williams, Chairman of the Board of Trustees of the University of Pennsylvania and a former student of Professor Smith, September 19, 1958; Dr. Joseph H. Willits in charge of the Educational Survey of the University of Pennsylvania and one of Professor Smith's former students, May 18, 1959; Charles A. Madison, editor of the college textbook division of Henry Holt and Company, June 15, 1959.

LETTERS TO THE AUTHOR FROM SMITH'S ASSOCIATES

The author received letters from the following: Dr. Hugh H. Bennett, Dr. George F. Carter, Spencer Chase, Morris Llewellyn Cooke, H. L. Crane, Dr. Harry C. Diener, John Eisenhard, G. F. Gravatt, Dr. Richard Hartshorne, Margaret Hitch, Dr. Lester E. Klimm, Dr. Benjamin F. Lemert, Russell Lord, F. Webster McBryde, Dr. Howard H. Martin, Dr. E. Willard Miller, Dr. George J. Miller, Dr. George L. Slate, Dr. Otis P. Starkey, Dr. Walter Sheldon Tower, Dr. J. Russell Whitaker, Dr. Joseph H. Willits, Dr. Alfred H. Williams, Dr. Louis S. Wolfanger, and Dr. John K. Wright.

Many of the above are professional geographers, some of whom were Smith's former colleagues or students. Others listed are either those who are, or were, in the United States Department of Agriculture, or are members of various organizations to which Smith belonged. Still others are those who knew Smith in a capacity which shed light on his work.

Most of the above are cited in the text. All references can be found in the writer's personal files.

REVIEWS OF SMITH'S BOOKS

Boland, T. P. Review of *The Devil of the Machine Age.* *Commonweal*, XXXIV (June 6, 1941), 162.

Bowman, Isaiah. Review of *North America*. *Journal of Geography*, XXIV (July, 1925), 109.

Branom, Mendel E. Review of *Human Geography, Book One, Peoples and Countries. Journal of Geography.* XXI (February, 1922), 145.

Branom, Mendel E. Review of *Human Geography, Book Two, Regions and Trade. Journal of Geography*, XXII (January, 1923), 40.

Elkins, Annice Davis. Review of *Neighbors in the United States and Canada.* (J. Russell Smith and Frank E. Sorenson). *Journal of Geography*, XLVII (September, 1949), 260.

Halverson, L. H. Review of *American Lands and Peoples*. *Journal of Geography*, XXXII (March, 1932), 224.

Hutchinson, Keith. Review of *The Devil of the Machine Age*. *Nation*, CLII (April 19, 1941), 476.

Larson, Anna C. Review of *Our Industrial World*. *Journal of Geography*, XXXIV (May, 1935), 216.

Svec, M. Melvina. Review of *Neighbors Around the World*. *Journal of Geography*, XLVII (November, 1948), 337.

Svec, M. Melvina. Review of *Our Neighbors at Home*. (J. Russell Smith and Frank E. Sorenson). *Journal of Geography*, XLVII (November, 1948), 336.

Thompson, C. Bertrand. Review of *The Elements of Industrial Management*. *American Economic Review*, VI (June, 1916) 377–78.

Thralls, Zoe A. Review of *Home Folks*. *Journal of Geography*, XXVI (March, 1927), 121.

Wilson, Alla M. Review of *Foreign Lands and Peoples*. *Journal of Geography*, XXXIII (May, 1934), 384.

Woolbert, R. G. Review of *The Devil of the Machine Age*. *Foregin Affairs*, XX (January, 1942), 376.

Zon, Raphael. Review of *Tree Crops*. *American Economic Review*, XIX (June, 1929), 272.

MINUTES OF MEETINGS

Minutes of the Joint Committee on Graduate Instruction, Columbia University, Vol. I, March 18, 1911–May 16, 1922; Vol. II, October 31, 1922–May 19, 1939.

Index